# Microdosing Psilocybin Mushrooms

*An Essential Guide to Microdosing Magic Mushrooms & Microdosing Journal*

**Inspirational Creator**

rendering of legal, financial, medical or professional advice. The content within this book has been derived from various sources. Please consult a licensed professional before attempting any techniques outlined in this book.

By reading this document, the reader agrees that under no circumstances is the author responsible for any losses, direct or indirect, that are incurred as a result of the use of the information contained within this document, including, but not limited to, errors, omissions, or inaccuracies.

ISBN 978-1-922940-06-3 (E-book)

ISBN 978-1-922940-07-0 (Paperback)

Cover Design by Andav

Published by Inspirational Creator

Bil Harret & Anastasia V. Sasha

First Edition (2023)

# Table of Contents

Introduction .................................................. 8

Chapter 1: Microdosing ................................. 15
    When It All Began ................................... 17
    Does Microdosing Work? ......................... 19
    The Neuroscience Behind Psilocybin ...................... 25

Chapter 2: Microdosing for Health Benefits ................ 31
    Medicinal and Mental Health Applications ............ 32
    Improving Your Well-Being .................................. 48
    Social Benefits ........................................... 51

Chapter 3: All You Need to Know Before Starting Microdosing ............................................... 57
    How to Find Your Optimal Dose ............................ 58
    Where Can You Find Psilocybin? ........................... 60
    Drying ..................................................... 63
    Long-Term Storage ............................... 69

Chapter 4: Ready to Get Started ................................. 73
    Microdosing Protocols ........................................... 74

Synergic Stackings .................................................. 80

Best Microdosing Practices ..................................... 83

Chapter 5: Possible Adverse or Common Side Effects 89

Who Is Disqualified From Microdosing? ................ 90

Possible Side Effects .............................................. 95

Chapter 6: Legality ................................................. 101

Decriminalization Versus Legalization .................. 101

Drug Testing and Other Questions ........................ 104

Conclusion ............................................................ 109

Microdosing Journal ............................................... 111

Dear Reader ........................................................... 181

References ............................................................. 183

# Introduction

Timothy Leary, an American psychologist, said that in the course of a few hours after taking psilocybin, he learned more about the mind than he had in his entire career of over fifteen years.

Psychedelics have been known to alleviate numerous health issues, including mental disorders like depression, anxiety, and OCD, when normal pharmacology simply doesn't seem to work. If you are reading this book, you are either interested in using psilocybin mushrooms to improve your health, help someone else, or just find out a bit more about microdosing and the healing power of psilocybin.

Used in holistic medicine, microdosing is the self-administration of a psychedelic substance (like psilocybin) at one-tenth, one-twentieth, or even as little as one fiftieth of the normal dose. You experience the substance's benefits—like improvements in mood or migraine relief—without it interfering with your regular functioning and daily life.

Microdosing practices can also be tailored to your lifestyle and needs, but they do involve an empirical factor when finding your optimal dose. It's recommended to start low, within the recommended range, and slowly increase it over time until you begin experiencing the desired effects.

You may be less familiar with the word "psilocybin" than you are with "magic mushrooms." Psilocybin is the main active compound found in over two hundred Psilocybin mushroom species, such as *Psilocybe*, *Panaeolus*, and *Conocybe* mushrooms. Psilocybin is converted into the pharmacologically active chemical psilocin in the digestive tract after ingestion, this conversion process is known as dephosphorylation. Psilocybin is a "prodrug", meaning it has to be converted to become active. Psilocin is the compound that's primarily responsible for the euphoric effect and has the ability to activate your serotonin receptors (most notable the serotonin 5-HT2A receptor) and dopamine pathways.

While psilocybin gained widespread popularity in the late 1950s, it is likely that mushrooms containing psilocybin were ingested by our ancestors, stretching between several million and 10,000 years ago, with the earliest evidence being found in Northern Australia. Rock art representing the effects of magic mushrooms in ancient drawings of a person with the head of a mushroom was discovered. This art suggested that these mushrooms were used in ceremonies to help people connect on a higher, spiritual level, as well as for medicinal purposes, by tribes indigenous to America and Europe for thousands of years.

Its popularity went underground after being classified a U.S. Schedule I controlled substance (making it illegal to buy, possess, or use) on October 27, 1970. However, the rise of psilocybin's popularity in the last few years has encouraged scientists to start studying its numerous benefits again despite issues regarding its legality.

In a clinical development programme called COMPASS—spreading through North America to Europe—scientists managed to create a synthesized version of psilocybin called "COMP360" in capsule forms of 1 mg, 10 mg, and 25 mg. Revolutionary centers all over Europe have conducted therapy that aims to try to prove that psilocybin could be an effective medical treatment option for drug-resistant patients, ranging from people with depression right through to other mental and physical illnesses. This trial incorporates psychology with pharmacology, and the therapists involved in this treatment programme have to be FDA approved (Compass News, 2022).

According to these statistics, one single 25 mg intake of psilocybin can drastically reduce depressive symptoms and suppress them for up to three months (Rucker et al., 2022). Please be aware that a 25 mg dose of psilocybin is considered a high dose, equivalent to having somewhere over 3 g of dried psilocybin mushrooms, depending on their potency, which would lead to a very intense experience. Unfortunately, these studies are all still at the trial stage and it could be many years before any FDA-approved psilocybin medication will be available on the market. I will cover the main reasons for this at the end of this book.

Psilocybin mushrooms are genetically made up of constituents other than just psilocybin and psilocin. With different concentrations, depending on the strain of mushroom, other hallucinogenic compounds researchers have not yet studied in such detail include but are not limited to baeocystin, bufotenin, and norpsilocin. Studies comparing the results of psilocin with the other mentioned compounds present (using the whole mushroom body) to isolated psilocin in rats found the compounds working together to be more effective in reducing anxiety levels and changing behavioral responses. (Matsushima et al. 2009 and Zhuk et al. 2015) The compound psilocybin will always be given orally and, once ingested, it will get broken down into psilocin. Never ever try to inject psilocybin. This can be lethal. If researchers are using the drug intravenously, it's not psilocybin but a synthetic version of psilocin.

Tracy, a good friend of mine, decided to go the psychedelic microdosing route a few months ago to try an alternative to the antidepressant she started taking two years earlier to improve her mental health. She felt stuck, gloomy, irritated, and not her usual self. She was never the cheerleader, nor happy, bouncy type, but lately, something inside her felt off balance.

She was diagnosed with depression, a mental-health issue that can be inherited, which ran in her family. As a teen, she was put on a prescription drug that seemed to help for a while.

Eventually, the pills didn't work as well anymore. Researching after a conversation we had about psilocybin therapy and how it impacted my life, and with her psychiatrist also present,, she came across a study that was published about the benefits of psilocybin. The study claimed how these mushrooms helped patients with terminal illnesses cope with their feelings of fear, anxiety, and depression. After more research, Tracy realized that psilocybin is not only helping mental health patients. Many people claim it helps with physical issues such as cluster headaches too.

Desperate, she decided to go ahead and try a single, low dose of dried psilocybin mushrooms and I remember she stated, "It took effect and lifted my mood instantly. I remember feeling some kind of healing within. It's hard to describe. I was so happy I couldn't sleep that night." She then tried small quantities, spread out over a couple of days, following some microdosing instructions she found, which kept her spirit lifted and made her feel happier. The world wasn't so dreary anymore and she started having more fun in her life again.

Almost 300 million people suffer from depression and one out of every 10 people suffers from some mental health disorder, making mental illness one of the major causes of disability and ill health globally (Dattani et al., 2021). Tracy's condition is quite common.

Microdosing with psilocybin could minimize the symptoms of depression and other mental health issues like anxiety, obsessive-compulsive disorder (OCD), and post-traumatic stress disorder (PTSD). But these aren't the only benefits you could experience. This substance, when used correctly, could prevent migraines and cluster headaches, decrease the impact of ADHD symptoms, improve mood and cognitive functioning, increase relational skills and productivity, promote introspection and self-realization, stimulate brain growth and brain restoration, minimize the occurrence of inflammation in the body, and stave off chronic pain. We will cover many of the mentioned benefits in more detail later in the book, along with others not yet mentioned.

This could help many people suffering from a range of ailments, but those who decide to microdose at home need to ensure they do it properly. This includes measuring the correct intake of psilocybin, among other important factors we will be discussing. For instance, if you take a little more, it won't poison you, but you might start feeling the typical effects of the so-called "trip," which should wear off in a few hours. This might include hallucinations, a spike in anxiety, or even a bad trip if you don't expect it. And taking too little may not provide any noticeable benefits. Additionally, you cannot take doses daily because while psilocybin tolerance fades quickly when the course is interrupted, it builds up pretty fast.

After not only observing but also experiencing the benefits of psilocybin, I understood why Paul Stamets, a well-known American mycologist, believes that mushrooms are nature's messengers. Mother nature has provided humankind with many natural remedies. But just like with any type of medication, natural or not, there could be negative side effects. I wrote this book to not only share the potential beneficial qualities of these versatile mushrooms, but to also provide you with everything you need to know to begin your own microdosing journey and safely increase your health.

Whether you are looking to improve your health, slow down and enjoy your life, or you are simply curious about microdosing, you have all the information and tips you need to start. But first, you must understand how microdosing works and the possible effects of psilocybin on your brain before planning and creating your unique microdosing practice. Chapter 1 will provide you with that foundation.

# Chapter 1: Microdosing

*This possibility to change reality, which exists in everyone, represents the real freedom of every human individual.* –Albert Hofmann

The "mind shift" took less than one month and a single low dose of 1 g of dried *Psilocybe mexicana* that Zeb, an Irish friend I met in Puerto Morelos (Mexico), prepared for me in the form of a chocolate bar. Something happened when I took it, something that would allow me to immerse myself in the present in a way I forgot was even possible.

It was a very humble dose, so the walls of the room were not breathing or anything like that, but the music sounded particularly different, like it was coming from within while driving my emotions. I still remember that profound sense of inner peace after taking it, saying to myself, "Why can't I simply feel this way without having this substance?" That was probably the question that changed everything.

Jo, another Irish friend, turned up an hour later, sent by her twin sister to make sure I was fine. When she opened the door, I was mesmerized. Her dress was gleaming, and its colorful design of dots looked like it was coming out from the dress while hypnotizing me.

"Are you feeling okay?" she asked while smiling.

Jo is the kind of person with a smiley face, so it felt great to simply see her. I asked, "How will the hangover be tomorrow?"

"Hangover? Tomorrow you will feel great," she said.

I asked her if it was a good idea to go outside, and she replied with another big smile, like knowing exactly what was about to happen, "We surely can."

We went outside, and... simply... wow! Even though I was in the same place as the previous three days, I was absolutely stunned by the views and the bright colors. If you are curious, the views on the front were to the ocean, and on the back were to the jungle, on which the last rays were shining before nightfall. The beauty was there all the time, but now I was able to see it. It was like witnessing two different worlds when focusing my attention on each one of them. There was also a saxophone player playing somewhere in the backstreet between my hotel and the jungle, and it felt like the notes were spreading all over the jungle. It was beyond a dream.

That evening was extremely magical, adding to the fact that we all joined together to watch the blood moon occuring that night at the oceanfront. Like Jo had anticipated, the day after I felt reborn. The anxiety that often had me worrying over future events just started fading, and it kept fading away since that moment. How? Was it the substance? Was it me? I'm not sure how it happened or what would have happened if I hadn't had it, but psilocybin was certainly a turning point.

Understanding how microdosing came to be is important. It explains its recent rise in popularity, while also assuring us that this practice is not simply a new trend. This is important, because having a detailed understanding of psilocybin and its effect on your mind is critical to ensuring you take the correct safety precautions while microdosing. This means understanding how psilocybin therapy began.

## When It All Began

It's common for shamans from cultures all over the world to ingest mushrooms containing psilocybin with the aim of triggering a spiritual experience. This includes contacting their people's ancestors, spirits, gods, or even the universe itself, depending on their beliefs. In general, they use psilocybin to get in touch with their higher self, to answer complicated questions, and even to find inner peace. While shamans have used psychedelic substances for many years, it was Terence McKenna's "stoned ape theory" that sparked the idea that mushrooms containing psilocybin could be responsible for our evolution from *Homo erectus* to *Homo sapiens*.

There are many versions of how mankind evolved from apes to *Homo sapiens*, but I bet you have never been introduced to the "stoned ape theory." We have all heard of the so-called "missing link," that one piece in the puzzle of evolution that can explain why the brain exploded and the human cortex tripled in size in such a small, ridiculous period of time when viewed from an evolutionary perspective. But what was the trigger?

In 1992, Terence McKenna wrote a book, *Food of the Gods*, which explains how magic mushrooms propelled *Homo erectus* to evolve into *Homo sapiens*. Cattle were domesticated animals, and some magic mushroom species thrive in animal dung. It's suggested that our ancestors ate these mushrooms and—as research has shown how psilocybin creates and enhances new neural pathways in the brain—began to move away from animal-like thinking, growing a new self conscious, changing the meaning of time, and allowing information to be processed on a much higher level.

The status of these fascinating mushrooms went from zero to extremely popular in the late 1950s when a traveler, Gordon Wasson, accidentally came across a tribe performing a ceremony with the now-famous fungi while he was on holiday in Mexico. He was so impressed with the mushroom's potential as a natural healer and medium for soul-searching that he brought back a sample. Wasson gave this sample to his Swiss chemist friend, Alfred Hoffman—who is more commonly known as "the father of LSD"—who along with his team isolated, named, and synthesized the main compounds known as "psilocybin" and "psilocin." His discovery triggered the start of clinical trials.

At this time, scientists and researchers wanted to determine whether psilocybin could be used as a treatment option for different psychiatric illnesses, from depression to schizophrenia, autism, and even obsessive-compulsive disorders. Psilocybin has been researched since the 1960s to determine its potential to increase wellness, enhance emotional, spiritual and mental healing, and serve as a possible mood lifter for terminally ill patients.

Psilocybin has an extensive research history aimed at determining its therapeutic and medical benefits. Since 1970, when it was classified as a Schedule I drug, it has been considered a dangerous drug with the potential of being abused for its hallucinogenic qualities. As psilocybin is still an illegal substance at present—which I will elaborate on more in Chapter 6—it becomes difficult for researchers to gain the permission and funding needed to conduct clinical trials. But there are still quite a few ongoing studies available to help us better understand whether microdosing with psilocybin works.

## Does Microdosing Work?

While the "war on drugs" started by the US federal government suppressed the research that could be conducted by working with psychedelics, psilocybin has recently re-emerged as a therapeutic agent for treating mental illness and improving well-being. Many people are skeptical about the benefits of psychedelics, which is understandable after all that I mentioned, but let's look into it.

Anecdotal evidence takes the form of verbal accounts of a person's experience and may include reports, surveys, and other forms of feedback, depending on a person's unique experience. Hundreds of thousands of individual reports with consistent data state the benefits of microdosing with psilocybin mushrooms, but all are deemed anecdotal evidence because they do not meet the scientific criteria to be considered empirical evidence, which is scientifically more reliable.

Empirical evidence is the information scientists obtain through experimentation and observation. It normally includes clinical trials and scientific studies. Having said that, there are many small, private studies that have been funded by enthusiasts claiming that psilocybin does have many health benefits, but not all of them have been proven beyond a shadow of a doubt in a lab that has every protocol in place, making a number of them more circumstantial than empirical.

For the time being, both the anecdotal and empirical evidence currently available to us seem to support the possibility of using psilocybin microdosing to improve your mental health, to improve physical performance, and even to treat diseases like migraines. Let's take a look at some of these studies.

## *Anecdotal Versus Empirical Evidence*

When looking at the various anecdotal benefits and emergent research, we can see that people do seem to benefit from microdosing with psilocybin. Early studies conducted before psilocybin became illegal show that psilocybin targets the brain's serotonin receptors. Serotonin is a chemical that's often relates to feelings of happiness and positivity, but it also plays an important role in your ability to learn and remember things. It's believed that the reported positive effects of microdosing with psilocybin are related to its interactions with these receptors.

Due to issues regarding its legality, there is more anecdotal evidence available to us compared to empirical research. But the evidence that is available provides us with useful information supporting the reported benefits of microdosing. Fortunately, its rise in popularity since 2015 has allowed for new research to take place, providing us with recent, updated reports that support the information we originally had regarding the impact of psilocybin on the brain. From these reports, there was a general consensus that microdosing with psilocybin can improve your mood and mental health.

In 2018, an international survey was conducted with the aim of determining whether a person's mental health could be improved by microdosing with psychedelics, including substances like psilocybin and LSD. Out of the

1,102 participants, 44% reported that they experienced improvements in their mental health (Lea et al., 2020). This is one of the many studies that support the potential benefits of microdosing. While it may be based on the experiences of various individuals, the results of this study are supported by another study conducted in October 2020.

This latter study aimed to gain a more detailed understanding of how psilocybin specifically could impact those who used it to microdose. Researchers gathered their data from the Global Drug Survey (GDS) 2019 and looked at individuals who microdosed with psilocybin in the last 12 months. Participants reported improvements in their mood, sociability, focus, and creativity. Additionally, reports stated no challenges while microdosing, which was unlike their experience taking common, legal medications (Petranker et al., 2020).

Patients who have been diagnosed with cancer often develop additional, clinically significant symptoms of depression and anxiety. In recent years, a study aimed to determine empirically the impact of psilocybin on these symptoms using a randomized, double-blind, cross-over trial. The cross-over took place five weeks after the administration of a microdose (aiming to minimize the placebo response) of 1 to 3 mg per 154.32 lb (70 kg) first and a high dose of 20 mg to 30 mg per 154.32 lb (70 kg) second, or vice versa. Researchers found that participants experienced larger decreases in their symptoms of anxiety and depression with the high dose in comparison to the single microdose (92% versus

32%), their quality of life and sense of optimism towards death improved, and life felt more meaningful. These benefits were sustained for six months after the completion of the trial, with a continued decrease in anxiety and depression (Griffiths et al., 2016).

One of the biggest studies done to date worldwide at the University of British Columbia, with over 4,000 participants from 75 countries using an anonymous self-reporting system, found a clear association between microdosing and a mass improvement of depression and anxiety symptoms in individuals who followed a microdosing regimen of psilocybin or LSD, compared to those who didn't microdose.

However, more clinical trials and studies need to be conducted to gain a better understanding of the exact impact of psilocybin, including the microdosing practices. The strongest evidence that comes to my mind to know with certainty if microdosing psilocybin works would be an enormous randomized placebo-controlled trial (RCT) where thousands of individuals would be randomly chosen, and a placebo given to half of the participants.

### Talking About the Placebo

A placebo is a substance that is inert (has no effect on your mind or body) and is used in controlled experiments like clinical studies to determine the efficiency of another substance. The *nocebo*, however, is a substance that could worsen symptoms due to the patient's negative expectations. The mind is powerful, and when it believes that something is working, chances are you will start experiencing the improvements and benefits you are expecting. While some researchers believe it's important to account for a person's positive and negative beliefs regarding the effectiveness of microdosing, other researchers, like James Fadiman, believe that if a person strongly believes that microdosing is working for them, then there's no harm in it.

Besides the difficulties regarding psilocybin's legality, the use of a placebo and nocebo can also present their own unique challenges. These challenges usually relate to how researchers conduct their studies, but there is currently a self-blinding study that was conducted to specifically explore the effects of a placebo on psychedelic microdosing.

This particular study aimed to determine whether psychedelic microdosing could improve an individual's cognitive functioning and psychological well-being. Participants were split into two groups. Group one was given the psychedelic microdose, while group two received the placebo microdose. Neither group was told whether they were receiving the placebo or the psychedelic compound. This form of control allowed researchers to ensure the results they obtained were due to the impact of the drug itself and not the participant's belief of how the drug impacted them. Their results demonstrated that microdosing could improve a person's well-being, mental health, and satisfaction with life; however, the participants who were given the placebo were also shown to improve. The overall result of this study was that the placebo effect of microdosing may play a large role in helping you experience the expected benefits (Szigeti et al., 2021).

Researchers are torn between concrete evidence of patients who claimed they experienced positive effects during the intake of psilocybin, and those who believed they felt better, yet were given a placebo. Could microdosing facilitate an improved placebo response in healthy individuals? Microdosers' expectations clearly have some influence on the reported outcomes. However, further research is needed because studies so far have focused on macrodosing over microdosing, and mostly in the short term effects of microdosing, and it may be that its benefits only emerge in the long term. Additionally, there is no clinical trial of microdosing available conducted only on healthy individuals. There might be particular clinical benefits to specific conditions. But let's jump to the next section, where you will get a better understanding of psilocybin's effect on your brain.

## The Neuroscience Behind Psilocybin

Psilocybin is a chemical compound that can change and alter the neural networks, as well as the different regions, in our brains. Neurotransmitters allow communication throughout the brain and body. On an average day, our neurons are firing continuously and use our neurotransmitters as pathways to get from point A to point B. If you think of the brain as a map and our neurotransmitters as roads, the neurons would be the vehicles traveling back and forth on this road.

Psilocybin has the power to create new side roads that lead to completely unexplored destinations, or it can "rebuild" a network by reconnecting two pathways that became structurally unstable, allowing the neurons to use it again. Psilocybin can allow the brain to overhaul networks, remodel thought patterns, follow new thinking patterns, and rewire the mind. If we look at our brain as a master computer, psilocybin could be used as a software program to restart, adjust, and increase the computer's internal processor.

A study that was conducted showed that under the influence of psilocybin, a decrease in the connectivity between areas of the brain responsible for planning and decision making were observed; however, this study also demonstrated an increase in connectivity between areas involved in sensation and movement (Dolan, 2020). This could explain the psychedelic state that occurs when higher doses of psilocybin are ingested.

Scientists suggest that psilocybin allows different regions of the brain to communicate, especially in people who suffer from depression, modifying long-held patterns and deep-rooted pathways, ultimately freeing the person. Other areas are muted, and the brain region that plays a role in keeping the sense of self is one of them. This area might be over connected in depressed people, and loosening these connections could decrease depression instead of numbing their feelings like antidepressants do. This could allow the brain a chance to restructure itself, completely diminishing feelings of depression and other psychiatric conditions.

Psilocybin could ease anxiety and other mental ailments by changing the default mode network in the brain—a region responsible for meditative thought processes and creating one's sense of perception—by making use of a treatment regime of low doses, over an extended period.

The human brain has the capacity to grow and change as you get older. This ability is known as "neuroplasticity," and psychedelics may have the potential to boost your brain's capacity for neuroplasticity. A study conducted on mice found that small doses of psilocybin had the potential to increase the growth of new brain cells in the hippocampus, known as "neurogenesis," while higher doses reduced this growth (Smith, 2021).

The hippocampus is the part of the brain responsible for learning and memory. Its capacity for neuroplasticity is vital as it can influence the strength of the connections between your neurons. This can play an important role in your psychological well-being. People suffering from depression might become less emotionally avoidant as their cognitive functioning starts to increase and the mind begins to think in a different manner. We don't yet know if the same thing happens in the human brain, but this study implies that dosage is a critical factor when you aim to experience certain benefits.

Additionally, there is another area of the brain known as the "claustrum," found in the prefrontal cortex, which has access to all regions of the mind. Its main function is to create our sense of self-awareness and the conscious. Psilocybin modifies the communication between the different areas of the brain and the claustrum, and affects memory, auditory and executive functioning, and affects spirituality.

Roland Griffiths is a professor and one of the cornerstone lecturers in psychiatry and neurosciences at the Johns Hopkins University School of Medicine. Griffiths has been involved in a pilot study testing whether psilocybin and psychotherapy can ease end-of-life anxiety in cancer patients. According to *The British Journal of Psychiatry*, reports have shown that psilocybin can increase neural activity in brain regions related to memory, and people can recall events from their past much faster and in more detail. Microdosing has been linked to memory enhancement, opening new doorways for hidden, pent-up emotions in patients struggling to deal with their feelings, and an overall positive effect related to mood, mental health, cognition, and creativity.

# Key Takeaways

- Psilocybin may have played a crucial role in our evolution from *Homo erectus* to *Homo sapiens*.

- Studied for many years despite legality issues, psilocybin has shown great potential.

- Both anecdotal and empirical evidence support psilocybin's potential ability to manage and treat a number of health issues, as well as improve your well-being.

- While a placebo may not provide you with any benefits, your belief in what it could do for you may play a role in your microdosing experience.

- Psilocybin has the ability to rewire your brain.

- Increasing your brain's capacity for neuroplasticity will allow your brain to grow, change, and adapt more easily in daily life.

- Dosage may play a vital role in determining the benefits you could experience with psilocybin.

We have traveled all the way through time from centuries ago, when aborigines were using psychedelics for spiritual purposes, to the 1950s when psilocybin was discovered and made popular by a traveler who accidentally stumbled upon the fungi and wrote an article about the benefits of the mushroom. He managed to send a sample to a scientist who created a synthetic version of the compound he isolated, called "psilocybin," and the rest is history, as they say. We have plowed through numerous studies, experiments, surveys, and trials searching for the answers to the secrets this compound might hold, including physical, mental, spiritual, and psychological health. I hope you are ready to start our next journey in Chapter 2, where we will find out exactly what this compound packs!

If you are enjoying this book so far, it would mean a lot to me if you could take a minute to review or rate it on the respective platform you acquired it from. Did you know that just 0.5 - 1% of readers do actually end up leaving a review? I have to admit that I used to not be that 1%, but now I do it different since I know how meaningful this can be to independent writers.

# Chapter 2: Microdosing for Health Benefits

*Mushrooms are miniature pharmaceutical factories, and of the thousands of mushroom species in nature, our ancestors and modern scientists have identified several dozen that have a unique combination of talents that improve our health.* –Paul Stamets

Daniel Carcillo, a retired NFL hockey player, used psilocybin microdosing to recover from the numerous concussions he had suffered during his illustrious career. Carcillo suffered seven major concussions and various sub-concussions, which resulted in a traumatic brain injury that negatively impacted many aspects of his life, causing him extreme headaches and severe sensitivity to the slightest light. His speech became slurred, his memory was shot, and he had trouble sleeping at night.

In a blink of an eye, Carcillo went from being a sports hero to experiencing suicidal depression. His brain injuries became so serious he couldn't even look at his phone's screen without pain, and his headaches made his life a living hell. Doctors had no cure, and his neurologist said his brain injuries are so traumatic that his life would never be the same again. After four years of trying to gain some type of quality of life, and with no cure and no desire left to live, Carcillo tried one last treatment option suggested by one of his teammates. A high dose of psilocybin was taken under supervision, and he found he could use his phone again within three days. Just under a month later, his clinical depression subsided.

His new calling in life was not to win another Stanley Cup final, but to raise enough money to create a new treatment that could help more than a million people suffering from traumatic brain injuries and diminish the suicide rate of helpless, hopeless TBI sufferers. Carcillo had to figure out his optimum doses and frequency on his own, but he managed to join Chad Bronstein and together they launched Wesana Health. The company began preclinical trials in 2021, after raising enough funds, and is hoping to begin human trials as soon as they can prove psilocybin is safe to use.

Magic mushrooms are still seen as illegal drugs, but many investors have noticed the potential of a medical breakthrough, and many companies are raising millions on the stock market, making research possible on a global scale!

# Medicinal and Mental Health Applications

Many studies are still being conducted on the benefits of microdosing with psychedelic substances; however, psilocybin has shown great promise in terms of medicinal and mental health applications. Although legality issues have made studying psilocybin's impact on a person's health more difficult (and more costly) than in other areas, many researchers have been able to obtain valuable information with the resources available to them. It's important that you refer to the studies I have discussed in this chapter and look at new studies, along with other studies not discussed here, so you can make informed decisions about how psilocybin could benefit you.

### *Depression*

Along with all the mentions related to depression in the neuroscience section, psilocybin's structural similarity to serotonin allows it to increase your brain's flexibility and make connections it may not normally make. This is called "brain entropy," and it can place your brain in a state that could allow it to restructure itself—known as "active coping"—to help you break free from your depressive state after only a single dose. In this way, psilocybin works opposite to antidepressants that dampen your depressive symptoms, known as "passive coping." But psilocybin can also help you process your emotions by reducing the activity in your amygdala. The amygdala is the part of your brain responsible for processing emotions. By reducing activity here, you may find it easier to process your emotions as your reaction to negative emotions becomes less harmful. This explains why studies focusing on psilocybin to treat depression, especially treatment-resistant depression, are popular.

## Treatment-Resistant Depression

When a person with depression has not responded to at least two different types of medication, nor experienced adequate relief from their symptoms, they are considered to have treatment-resistant depression. This type of depression can be difficult to manage, but psilocybin has emerged as a possible effective treatment. Do you remember the COMPASS program mentioned in the introduction? This study showed psilocybin had great effectiveness for people with treatment-resistant major depressive disorder. From a psychological overview, psilocybin allows these patients to access their subconscious, giving them the opportunity to look within to find the cause of their agony. Antidepressants were pharmacologically created to numb the patient without giving any insights into the cause, whereas psilocybin could help the person find answers and, ultimately, do the self-healing themselves.

## *Anxiety*

Psilocybin may positively affect your brain's blood flow which, combined with its ability to increase the brain's serotonin levels and ability to decrease the connectivity between areas of the brain responsible for planning and decision-making, could positively impact your levels of anxiety.

A double-blind placebo study aiming to explore the effects of microdosing with psilocybin on anxiety in patients with advanced-stage cancer found that microdosing was both safe and effective in significantly reducing participants' symptoms of anxiety, while also improving their mood and outlook on life (Grob et al., 2011).

## *Migraines and Cluster Headaches*

Migraines are a type of headache disorder and are considered an extremely debilitating health condition due to the severe pain experienced by those affected. Negatively impacting the lives of those who experience them, migraine sufferers often look for alternative treatments to manage their condition. Microdosing with psilocybin has emerged as an effective way to both prevent migraine attacks and reduce their occurrence.

The pain that accompanies a cluster headache is often, if not always, more severe and intense than the pain of a regular migraine. Unfortunately, there are a limited number of possible treatment methods for this condition, and not all of them work. Therefore, many patients who experience cluster headaches are more likely to use various legal and illegal substances to manage the intense pain that accompanies this condition. One study and different surveys found that psilocybin may have the potential to eliminate cluster headaches, or at least prevent their regular occurrence (Johnson and Griffiths, 2017).

A clinical investigation that aimed to gain a better understanding of the effect of psilocybin on migraines and cluster headaches ran a double-blind trial. They dosed a controlled group of adults with a placebo first, and then psilocybin two weeks later, during two sessions. Patients were given a microdose orally and were given headache diaries they needed to complete during the trial. Both mental and physical effects were monitored carefully, with follow-up sessions carried out to ensure protocols were followed at every step. The decrease in the frequency of migraines was significantly greater after psilocybin than after the placebo, and no withdrawal issues were noticed. These enduring therapeutic effects are a major find. Psilocybin might be the natural drug medical staff have been searching for to stop or at least alleviate the debilitating effects of these painful headaches (Schindler et al., 2020).

Participants from a different study reported a decrease in the severity of their migraines, confirming that microdosing may be a viable treatment (Dumka, 2021).

Jack suffers from migraines that impact his daily life, even with medical treatment. He was a bit skeptical at first about microdosing with psilocybin because it's a psychedelic drug, but he got to the point where he was willing to try anything. He began microdosing after I sent him a YouTube video titled "Micro-dosing: Saving Lives with Psychedelics|SBS The Feed." Through his unique microdosing practices, which included meditation and journaling to record his experience, Jack found that the occurrence of his migraines began to noticeably decrease, and when he did have one, it wasn't as severe as before. Jack was an old friend I met during my stay in Australia and even though I saw his improvements for a few months, unfortunately we are not in contact anymore to follow up on his experience.

## *Obsessive-Compulsive Disorder (OCD)*

When a person experiences a pattern of unwanted thoughts or obsessions, they may begin practicing repetitive behaviors, also known as "compulsions," that negatively impact their daily life and may cause the individual significant distress. If they try to stop the obsession, their anxiety will only increase. Repeating this behavior over and over is the only way for them to ease their distress. Obsessive Compulsive Disorder (OCD) is a frequent, and often devastating, mental health disorder that fixates on a behavioral ritual and impulsive routine that seems senseless or silly to others around them. Simple daily tasks are extremely difficult and even mundane activities feel impossible. OCD sufferers can be depressed, suicidal, and very anxious. Clinical trials have shown that microdosing with psilocybin may have the potential to reduce the negative symptoms of OCD.

A modified, double-blind study found that participants with OCD who were administered psilocybin experienced marked decreases in their symptoms. During the trial, it appeared that dosage didn't matter, as psilocybin seemed to produce an overall elimination of behaviors associated with OCD in animal model clinical trials (Matsushima et al., 2009). A more recent study found that OCD patients who microdosed with psilocybin had a substantial reduction in their symptoms (Johnson and Griffiths, 2017).

### Post-Traumatic Stress Disorder (PTSD)

After witnessing or experiencing a deeply terrifying and distressing event, a person may find it difficult to recover and cope, resulting in a condition called post-traumatic stress disorder (PTSD). Anxiety, fear, and flashbacks keep the person imprisoned, and they relive events that include accidents, natural disasters, deaths, or any life-threatening experience over and over. This can last for weeks, months, and even years. Some sufferers seem to snap out of their disorder naturally, but most are never cured.

PTSD is usually treated with antidepressant medication and regular visits to a psychiatrist or psychologist who offers cognitive processing therapy. This involves the patient evaluating their current setting and situation, restructuring their negative thought patterns, and transforming the way they feel over the event. Most of the time, treatment with medication and therapy doesn't help and many sufferers complete suicide. Microdosing with psilocybin has emerged as a possible effective treatment method.

In 2013, a study involving the University of South Florida claimed psilocybin's ability to modulate the serotonin synaptic concentrations helps the brain to grow and repair damaged cells located in the hippocampus, the brain's emotion and memory hub, which plays a role in how you feel and react in a situation, as well as helping you process and retrieve memories (Catlow et al., 2013). When a person goes through a traumatic experience, their brain's hippocampal volume decreases, and those with PTSD have the smallest volume. One study that focused on the impact of psilocybin on the hippocampal volume found that patients with combat-level PTSD who were treated with psilocybin, in addition to therapy, experienced an increase in their gray-matter volume, allowing for a reduction in their fear conditioning (Butler et al., 2018).

Additionally, psilocybin can also act on the amygdala (part of the brain responsible for mediating how you perceive fear) suppressing the fear conditioning that results in PTSD. Psilocybin may have the potential to effectively treat PTSD.

### *Neurogenesis and Neuroplasticity*

Psilocybin seems to enhance new neural pathways while diminishing old, "outdated" connections that do not serve the mind optimally. Our brains need to become accustomed to the modification of our neural pathways to change habits, learn new thinking processes, alter daily routines, and become more resilient. During our lifespan new brain cells get born, current cellular structures can change, and old cells die.

Psilocybin has the potential to act as a neurogenesis (brain growth) agent by promoting the brain-derived neurotrophic factor (BDNF). This is a powerful protein located in the central nervous system and the main regulator responsible for all the changes in these cells, activating development and renewal in several regions. This protein, and its levels in the brain, have been linked to disorders and mental conditions like bulimia, anorexia, Alzheimer's disease, dementia, and even Parkinson's disease. The higher our BDNF levels are, the easier we learn and remember, the less we stress, and the more we are capable of facing daily trials and tribulations.

Additionally, this molecule plays an important role in your brain's capacity for neuroplasticity. A study found that small doses of psilocybin had the potential to improve your brain's capacity for neuroplasticity, stimulating or activating plasma levels of BDNF to rise. However, while participants experienced increased neuroplasticity, it manifested in a way that was unique to each individual (Calder and Hasler, 2022). The aforementioned findings could be vital for the management and treatment of anxiety and depression, healing of brain injuries (Carcillo case), treating addiction, and possibly improving a person's cognition.

## *Attention Deficit Hyperactivity Disorder (ADHD)*

Many children and adults diagnosed with attention deficit hyperactivity disorder (ADHD) struggle with their attention span, impulsiveness, and hyperactivity. Psychedelics have been used for many years to treat ADHD; however, it was only recently that studies were aimed at understanding how microdosing with psilocybin could impact the mental and physical health of these individuals. There are various pharmacological treatments and medicines available, but many come with unpleasant side effects that may cause other physical problems like loss of sleep and a lack of appetite, leading to drastic weight loss and severe temper tantrums.

A survey published in the journal *Frontiers in Psychiatry* examined over 1,000 participants who used microdoses of psilocybin to help keep their ADHD in check. More than half the group said psilocybin helped them and seemed to be more effective than their medication, and a massive 80% claimed psilocybin lessened their symptoms drastically (Hutten et al., 2019).

One study found preliminary evidence that microdosing with psychedelic substances—like psilocybin and LSD—could help manage ADHD symptoms without any of the side effects commonly associated with ADHD medications. Participants also reported they switched from prescription stimulant medications to microdosing with psilocybin after the study, as they experienced more benefits and fewer side effects when microdosing (Totomanova, 2020).

However, more research is needed to ensure treatment remains beneficial and that patients are guaranteed to be safe on all levels. Psilocybin could change the quality of millions of lives globally. As a natural medicine, there would be a large decline in side effects, making it a safer treatment option for kids, teens, and adults.

## *Addiction*

It's quite amusing that psilocybin is deemed a drug with highly abusive qualities, but researchers and professionals claim it could be an extremely effective method and a low-risk way to help substance abusers stop their habits when addicted to dangerous, life-threatening substances. In the United States, over 100,000 individuals have perished after overdosing on opioids and other drugs in a single year (CDC, 2022).

The government supported many studies experimenting with psilocybin as a way to decrease relapses of substance abusers. A recent study, published in *Scientific Reports* on April 7, 2022, titled "Associations between classic psychedelics and opioid use disorder in a nationally representative U.S. adult sample," investigated over 200,000 participants who filled in the National Survey on Drug Use and Health (NSDUH) between the years 2015 and 2019, and discovered that anybody who was exposed to psilocybin was in less danger of getting hooked on opioids than those who never used magic mushrooms.

The study wasn't focused on psilocybin as a treatment option for addiction, but on finding connections between individuals who used drugs. However, professors were so impressed with the evidence they did have that a pilot study in 2017, conducted by Johns Hopkins University, was set up to see how many tobacco smokers who were introduced to microdoses of psilocybin could completely stop smoking for more than a year. Eighty percent of the participants became abstinent from smoking (Johnson and Griffiths, 2017).

A similar experiment was done using alcohol abusers in 2015. A psychiatric professor at the New York University Grossman School of Medicine recorded total abstinence from individuals who were addicted to alcohol after using psilocybin. Current experimental research from Garcia-Romeu has included psilocybin treatment to lower the dangers of substance users returning to substances like opioids, weed, and cocaine. Psilocybin can not only treat addiction, but it can also prevent and manage it.

## *Eating disorders*

The medical health field has begun investigating the possible benefits of using Psilocybin-assisted therapy to treat eating disorders, including anorexia nervosa. Psilocybin has the ability to rewire one's brain, potentially focusing on the root cause of eating disorders instead of just treating the symptoms.

The precise processes in the brain are not fully understood yet, but in theory, Psilocybin reduces or breaks down the default mode network (DMN). This network has established communication pathways between the different brain regions, sometimes creating certain misfit patterns; for example, eating without hunger or skipping meals. Over time, it becomes challenging to create new patterns, so we will stick to the established ones.

The default mode network seems to be overactive in certain mental health conditions, including eating disorders, and people can struggle with reasoning. Psilocybin could allow the brain to form new mental tracks by breaking those old patterns, providing the opportunity for the person to detect the true nature of these patterns and realize that, just like many social fears, these patterns are intended to help you, but are not adapted to reality, changing a person's point of view entirely.

## Other Medical Applications

Psilocybin has numerous medical and mental health applications. Unfortunately, not all of them have been studied in as much detail as those previously discussed. However, the information currently available on each topic is promising.

### Anti-Inflammatory Effects

In recent years, research done mostly using animal testing models has found that psilocybin may have the potential to act as an anti-inflammatory agent, minimizing inflammation in chronic pain conditions (Flanagan and Nichols, 2018). A South African study found, through a phytochemical analysis, that the *Psilocybe natalensis* mushroom, when administered at the right dosage, could have anti-inflammatory and antioxidant effects (Nkadimeng et al., 2020). However, more research is needed on this topic as not much is currently known about psilocybin's impact on inflammation in the human body.

### Alzheimer's Disease

We do know that psilocybin has the potential to reduce a person's anxiety levels, as well as its ability to act as an antidepressant, but it has also shown great potential as a possible aid for combatting early Alzheimer's disease. While most of the data we have pertaining to its impact on Alzheimer's disease has been conducted on animal models, preclinical data has shown that both high and low doses of psilocybin (administered in a safe and supportive setting) may be able to reverse brain atrophy (when neurons in the brain are lost), enhance a person's cognitive functioning, and slow down the progression of Alzheimer's disease. It's believed that these benefits may result from psilocybin's similarity to serotonin (both are indolealkylamines and are structurally similar) and its ability to positively affect how your memory functions (Garcia-Romeu et al., 2021).

## Diabetes

Although most of the information available on psilocybin's potential to control diabetes mellitus and its symptoms is based on anecdotal evidence, a study has found that the active components in mushrooms containing psilocybin were shown to exhibit anti-hyperglycemic and antidiabetic activity (Lo and Wasser, 2011). However, there is very little research pertaining to the effect of microdosing with psilocybin on diabetes.

## Color Blindness

Interestingly, microdosing with psilocybin has been reported by a number of individuals who are colorblind as having improved their ability to see color (Winstock, 2017). When a person ingests a psychedelic substance, the connections between their visual and linguistic cortical areas might be enhanced as the person's ability to perceive a situation and link concepts is impacted. Most of the information available has been based on the experiences of individuals who have taken psilocybin as a microdose, as well as a psychedelic dose. As such, the available preliminary data needs further clinical investigation before any solid conclusion is confirmed.

## Chronic Pain

Magic mushrooms have been used to alleviate pain, including discomfort caused by cancer, phantom limb pain, and cluster headaches. This potential to manage chronic pain may be linked to its possible ability to minimize inflammation. A small study followed three participants with chronic pain who had found no relief using common medications so they decided to try microdosing. The causes of their pain varied, but each participant practiced microdosing combined with functional exercises and ultimately found some relief (Lyes et al., 2022).

## Tinnitus

Tinnitus is when a person experiences ringing in their ears. Some users reported their condition disappeared after dosing or microdosing with psilocybin mushrooms, while others have reported that their condition either worsened or stayed the same. While tinnitus is unpleasant, microdosing with psilocybin will be something empirical if you suffer from this condition.

Additionally, psilocybin might help treat autism due to all the potential social benefits and what they involve, which we will discuss a few pages ahead. Microdosing psilocybin has also been used to treat premenstrual syndrome and premenstrual dysphoric disorder (more severe).

These are only some of the medical applications of microdosing with psilocybin. Through continued research, new information is becoming available to us. Don't be afraid to do your own research and investigate.

But psilocybin does not only benefit your health, it can also be used to improve your well-being.

## Improving Your Well-Being

Many of these aspects were briefly mentioned in the previous section, and while more research is needed to better understand psilocybin's impact, the information available has provided us with useful knowledge. In the section, I have discussed some of the main benefits you could experience.

### *Decreased Stress*

Psilocybin can alter your brain's levels of serotonin, positively impacting the prefrontal cortex. This part of the brain plays an important role in controlling a person's mood and perceptions. As such, microdosing with psilocybin has the potential to improve your mood and how you perceive the world around you, helping you to feel more relaxed and decreasing your stress levels. Many participants who participated in the previously mentioned study conducted by the University of British Columbia experienced lower levels of stress (Solis-Moreira, 2022).

### Improved Mood

Many individuals who microdose with psilocybin experience improvements in their mood and overall mental health. This may be owed to psilocybin's ability to activate your brain's serotonin receptors, as well as its structural similarity to this neurotransmitter. In a double-blind study, participants were given psilocybin to better understand its impact on their mood states with positive results (Kometer et al., 2012).

This was confirmed by a different study that observed greater improvements in the moods of participants who microdosed with psilocybin for one month compared to those who did not. (Rootman et al., 2022). Participants from a completely different study reported an improved outlook on life, a sense of optimism, emotional and spiritual insights, a sense of calm and peace, and greater feelings of happiness (Anderson et al., 2019).

### Creativity

Psilocybin affects your sense of self, emotions, perception, and cognition. These elements play an important role in your creativity. In the 1960s, clinical investigations into the effects of psilocybin found that those who were creative demonstrated various psychological traits that were similar to individuals under the influence of psilocybin (Sessa, 2008).

## *Productivity and Concentration*

Psilocybin can increase your productivity by boosting your energy levels and helping you focus by making your thoughts appear more clearly. One study found that participants experienced an increase in energy when they microdosed with psilocybin (Anderson et al., 2019). Another study found that small doses of psilocybin had the potential to increase a person's productivity, especially when they engaged in complex or cognitively-demanding tasks like academic work, software development, and engineering (Andersson and Kjellgren, 2019). This may result from similarities between the structure of psilocybin and serotonin.

## *Cognitive Functioning*

Cognitive functioning is related to your ability to think, learn new skills, remember things, speak, solve problems, interact with your surroundings, as well as a number of other abilities. Psilocybin's ability to positively impact your mood and mental health has been related to its ability to improve your cognitive functioning. The results of a study that aimed to explore the benefits and challenges of microdosing with psilocybin showed that a considerable number of the participants found their ability to understand a situation, solve a problem, recall information, and clearly think about it, had improved after microdosing (Anderson et al., 2019).

### *Enhanced Senses*

If you have ever taken a low or regular dose of magic mushrooms, it will likely make a lot of sense to you if I tell you that psilocybin has a strong impact on a person's visual perception and spatial orientation. But microdosing uses only one-tenth of a regular dose of psilocybin, so you should not experience any noticeable changes in how you perceive your surroundings. You'll know when it is *too* noticeable.

## Social Benefits

Could psilocybin facilitate social benefits? One study found that microdosing with psilocybin has a number of social benefits that allowed participants to overcome social challenges and improve their lives (Anderson et al., 2019).

## *Extraversion*

Oftentimes, socialization issues like stuttering and other mental health problems like anxiety and depression can make it difficult for a person to enjoy the outside world where other people are around. Affected individuals feel that it's easier and safer to stay isolated, but as humans, we are social creatures, and continued social isolation will often be detrimental to our mental health.

During my experiences with low doses of psilocybin, I remember a clear increase in my extraversion, relational skills, ability to read nonverbal language, and communicate. On several occasions, people who noticed this came up to talk to me. Right after my highest dosing experience with psilocybin, my partner and I were sitting outside of an Indian restaurant in Railay, Thailand, having dinner. A group sitting at another table changed to sit at a table next to us.

One of their members said to me, "You can smile with your eyes."

A conversation that took hours began. Later, they mentioned they had changed their table to sit next to us because they felt a "good energy" in my body language, especially when I looked at them. They became curious and decided to come and say "Hi."

On another occasion back in Waikiki (Hawaii), I saw this clearly in my friend Marco, where another girlfriend and I left him talking to a stranger on the beach. We were having a good time and went to get some beers, commenting on what the girl he was speaking to must be thinking. When we came back, she was sitting on our picnic mat with a big smile, super fascinated with the conversation they were having. Marco told me later that he never felt such clear thinking as in that moment, during their conversation.

Microdosing with psilocybin might be able to help you cope in social settings. A study found that psilocybin may increase a person's extraversion, especially in individuals with treatment-resistant depression (Erritzoe et al., 2018).

### *Empathy*

Empathy plays a crucial role in a person's moral and prosocial behavior. When your ability to show empathy towards others is impaired, you're at risk of serious social consequences that could negatively impact your mental health. A study investigating the effects of psilocybin on participants' empathic abilities found that there was a significant increase in their emotional and implicit empathy. These results were attributed to psilocybin's ability to alter how a person perceives a situation (Pokorny et al., 2017).

## Sense of Connection

While not specifically studied, many individuals who use psilocybin to microdose have reported that they experience intense feelings of interconnectedness, peace, love, and happiness; a higher-quality outlook on life, gratitude, hopefulness, and even realizations about who they are and where they are in life. Their thoughts become clear and cohesive, allowing them to think carefully when they are in a social situation.

We often forget that mental health and medical issues impact more than one aspect of our lives. It isn't until we have begun therapy, started medication, or used alternative therapies like microdosing with psilocybin that we realize exactly what we have been missing out on. I know cases of people who have been using antidepressant treatments for decades who, after changing to microdosing, started getting their emotions back! After all, you can't miss something you don't remember having experienced.

Additionally, users have claimed that their eating and sleeping habits improved, and they enjoyed their meditative practices, which help to keep them calm and grounded. Some stated they also drank less coffee, reduced or stopped their alcohol intake and drug use—such as weed, prescription drugs, and other illegal substances—and lived an overall healthier lifestyle. Others reported an increase in motivation, ambition, confidence, mindfulness, self-awareness of their surroundings, and open-mindedness. One thing all participants did agree on is that all the benefits seem to increase or rise as they continue to use low doses of psilocybin over extended periods of time.

Paul Stamets experienced something peculiar after accidentally taking a heroic, or macro dose of magic mushrooms. He had no prior experience, nor a clue of the dose he was taking and what was about to come. Stamets' experience was intense as he ended up sitting terrified at the top of a tree during a lightning storm, but he was able to ground himself by hugging that tree. You can check his trip report out in detail in the *Fantastic Fungi* documentary on Netflix.

What I came to share is that Stamets' stuttering was quite prevalent at that stage of his life, so in an instant in the middle of that storm, he started telling himself, "Stop stuttering." He repeated this phrase over and over again until the storm was over. Stamets climbed out of the tree and went home, straight to his bed. The next morning, Stamets was greeted by the woman he liked but had been too afraid to interact with before his psychedelic experience because of his stuttering. That morning, however, as she was passing by, he looked her in the eye and talked to her without stuttering once. From that moment onwards, Stamets' stuttering disorder was gone from his life.

Psilocybin seems to be a miracle compound that could cure brain diseases and increase the quality of life for many people suffering from illnesses and disorders. Psilocybin has great potential that deserves to be studied further. While researchers and microdosers face issues like the legality of this molecule, that should not stop you from learning about psilocybin's potential so you can draw your own conclusion about it.

## Key Takeaways

- Psilocybin has numerous potential benefits.

- Depression is often the main mental health issue studied, but psilocybin can benefit your mental and physical health in a variety of ways.

- Psilocybin has the potential to improve your general well-being, help you enjoy your life, and cope in social settings.

- Many of its potential benefits need more study, but the information currently available is promising.

While it's great to learn about the potential benefits you may experience while microdosing with psilocybin, you're probably wondering how you can practice microdosing when you don't know anything about it. That's where Chapter 3 comes in!

# Chapter 3: All You Need to Know Before Starting Microdosing

You may be slightly anxious about starting microdosing, but you don't need to be. Microdosing isn't complicated, and as long as you follow the guidelines, prepare the right dose, and use psilocybin responsibly, you can reap a number of benefits.

Some tools to consider before you begin your journey are a scale that is able to register one-hundredth of a gram if you want to begin with a low dose at first, and a strong grinder to create powder to mix into your food or drink, or pour the correct microdose amount into empty gel caps. Don't forget that psilocybin always has to be taken orally.

Everyone's dose will be unique, and what works for one person won't always work for someone else. Before getting started, remember that microdosing is not for everyone. If you have a family history of psychotic disorders or extreme mental conditions, such as bipolar disorder, any amount of psychedelics might overstimulate your senses. We will have a look at some adverse effects further on in the book.

# How to Find Your Optimal Dose

The honest answer to what your perfect dosage amount will be lies with you, depending on your ailment or reason for microdosing in the first place. A number of guidelines exist to help you find your optimal dose, but you also need to account for how psilocybin affects you individually and what your needs are. One of the key aspects to successfully microdosing is finding the right dose, which typically ranges between 0.1 g and 0.3 g of dried mushrooms, depending on the person, around one-tenth of a regular dose of psilocybin; however, some users go lower than 0.1 g, or higher, up to 0.5 g.

Your optimal dose will depend on different factors, including but not limited to the mushroom's potency, if the specimen is dry or fresh, your physical weight, other tryptamines involved, your own sensitivity to these tryptamines, and even the preparation and form of consumption. This could all sound very difficult to work out, but it's not. You can actually find low-cost kits that accurately measure potency levels.

It is recommended that you start with the smallest dose possible and work your way up incrementally by adding 0.05 g to each microdose as you feel comfortable and notice you have not yet experienced the benefits you are aiming for. In the same way, you will have to lower the dose when necessary.

Microdosing means the dose you take won't interfere with your daily functioning, so you shouldn't experience any of psilocybin's psychedelic effects. If you do increase your dose because you aren't sure if it's the right one yet, but find undesirable results or effects, then you can simply go back to your previous dosage. Once you have reached your optimal dose, you may notice you're getting the benefits you were looking for: sleeping better, enhancing your mood, eating healthier, falling interest in drinking alcohol or caffeine, losing interest in habits like smoking, having caffeine or drinking alcohol, or even feeling like you are becoming a "better" version of yourself; while you forgot you took any substance. These occurrences indicate you have hit your sweet spot. If your goals are looking to immerse yourself in nature, go to a musical event, induce more introspective thinking, or become more social, your optimal dose might need to be slightly higher.

### *Typical Magic Mushroom Doses:*

- Microdose: 0.1–0.5 grams.

- Low Dose: 0.5–1 gram.

- Moderate Dose: 1–3 grams.

- High Dose: 3–5 grams and above.

## *Typical Psilocybin Doses:*

- Microdose: < 4 mg.

- Low dose: 4–8 mg.

- Average dose: 6– 20 mg.

- High dose: 20–35 mg.

# Where Can You Find Psilocybin?

Before I discuss possible sources of psilocybin, you have to check the laws and regulations of both the country and state you live in as these do differ. Psilocybin has a number of legality issues surrounding it despite its rise in popularity among the public and in the scientific community. Once you are aware of what is and isn't allowed, you can decide where you will source your psilocybin from. Unfortunately, legality issues mean you can't simply buy it from an online supplier; however, there are other ways of obtaining mushrooms containing psilocybin, but they all come with their own risks.

## *Foraging*

Searching for mushrooms containing psilocybin in the environment you live in is a popular method, but it means you need to have a good understanding of this practice. Most mushroom poisoning cases that occur result from incorrect identification. Many mushrooms look similar, and while some cause mild poisoning, others can be deadly. Sometimes, the difference in appearance is minimal. There are an estimated 1.5 million species in the fungi kingdom, with 90% yet to be discovered, so you should be really careful! As such, foraging can be tricky, but probably not as tricky as you think if you take it seriously and are willing to learn about it.

You have to know what kind of mushroom grows best during which season, as well as what type of environment the mushroom you are looking for prefers. There are a number of mushroom species that contain psilocybin, and they all thrive in different environments. Psilocybin mushrooms are plentiful in nature and if you look in the right areas, you can get very lucky, especially during the fruiting season. They might even be hiding in your backyard, depending on where you live of course.

You can read through the third part of my previous manual, *Psilocybin Mushrooms 3 in 1,* to identify the main *Psilocybe* species and start with the basics; otherwise, you can do some research online. A beginner will have a better chance to correctly identify a species such as *Psilocybe cubensis,* instead of a specific strain (subspecies) that can be tricky even for your top expert. You can ask more experienced mushroom foragers to teach you and double-check your harvested mushrooms to ensure they are the correct species (very important); or, you can take pictures of your foraged mushrooms and upload them to an online forum or Facebook group where experienced mushroom foragers can help you identify them correctly.

## *Cultivating*

If you aren't comfortable with the previous option but you are willing to cultivate your mushrooms, you can either source the spores in the wild or from a reputable online supplier (be aware of scammers) and build your own growing station, or you can buy a grow kit.

The grow kit includes a growth chamber (like a plastic tub), a fully colonized substrate (the medium the mushrooms need to grow in), and the spores. The grow kit is more expensive, but you are basically skipping the incubation part and moving straight to the fruiting phase, where contamination is far less likely. And as long as you read your manual carefully and follow the instructions, you should have a successful harvest!

If you want to learn to cultivate your own mushrooms at a low cost, there are many ways to do so. In my other books, I go into detail about the main cultivation methods and everything else you need to get started. If you would like to find out more, I invite you to check out my previous book. For now, just remember to harvest your mushrooms before they drop their spores, and expect additional flushes. But how do you prepare your mushrooms for microdosing and storing?

## Drying

Once you harvest your mushrooms, you must dry and store them properly if you want to use them for the next few months. If you don't, they will become moldy and decompose within a matter of days. Mushrooms contain a high volume of moisture and are made up of 90% water. Anything that is loaded with moisture attracts mold and bacteria, and once your mushrooms get infected, the mold can spread like wildfire. You have to dry your mushrooms properly because even a tiny bit of moisture can cause microbes to contaminate your harvest.

We want bone-dry mushrooms. However, you also have to be careful about what temperatures you use to dry your mushrooms to avoid potency loss. Many users suggest keeping the temperature below 212°F (100°C), but there is no real evidence at the time this book is being written that suggests psilocybin starts to degrade at any given temperature. We just know that psilocybin is sensitive to heat and that the degradation rate

63

increases when the temperature increases, particularly over 212°F (100°C). Hence, we will try to avoid unnecessarily high temperatures.

It's best to dry a number of mushrooms, of varying sizes, and store them dried but whole to avoid potency loss (I will get into this later). You probably know that psilocybin concentration can differ substantially among the different strains and species, as well as between specimens of the same group. But did you know caps have a higher potency than stems, and different parts of the mushroom have various tryptamine levels? For this reason, you can grind them every week into a powder that is thoroughly mixed to make a homogenous mass, resulting in a relatively stable potency. This powder can then be used to prepare your microdosing capsules for the week. A mortar and pestle or a coffee grinder will work best.

Before you decide on a drying method, you will have to cut off any part of the stem that is covered in substrate and clean your mushrooms, wiping off any visible dirt. Do not use water to clean them, it is not recommended because this increases the moisture levels and the risk of contamination and decomposition. After your mushrooms have been cleared, you can begin the drying process. Your goal is to dry your mushrooms to the point that they become brittle and break. We will first look at a couple of drying methods, and then we will explore storage.

Before moving to any drying method, you can first pre-dry your mushrooms to ensure better results. Pre-drying is easy. Place your mushrooms on a dry towel or piece of cardboard. If you use a towel, you may need to replace it several times to ensure no moisture is re-absorbed. Place this board or towel out of direct sunlight in a well-ventilated area (you can also help it with a fan). The perfect conditions are around 86 °F (30 °C) and a humidity below 55%. Once your mushrooms look wrinkly and feel rubbery when touched, the pre-drying process is complete. You can then move on to drying your mushrooms using one of three methods.

### *Dehydrator*

Dehydrating your mushrooms is the best way to dry them. While dehydrators are typically quite expensive, they are a useful investment because you can use them not only to dehydrate your mushrooms for microdosing but to also dehydrate other foods that you can snack on like strawberries, regular mushrooms for cooking, etc. Remember, heat and mushrooms are not great friends. The higher the temperature, the quicker the mushroom degrades and the more tryptamines diminish. Mushrooms also don't like sunlight. This is why you should use a dark towel to cover your mushrooms when air-drying them under the sun.

The larger mushrooms will go on the top ring tray (where heat is higher), while the smaller ones get placed on the bottom ring tray. Spread your mushrooms out on the dehydrator trays, ensuring none of the mushrooms are touching each other, and place the trays back in the dehydrator. If you are using a vertical dehydrator, put the biggest mushrooms closest to the fan and arrange them from medium to small going outwards, leaving the tiny mushrooms furthest from the fan. Set your dehydrator to 110°F or 40°C. This device uses gentle heat and constant airflow to remove the remaining moisture from your mushrooms. The process could take between four and eight hours, so set a timer and check your mushrooms every two hours. Once your mushrooms can snap when pressure is applied to them, like a potato chip, they are ready to be stored.

### *Air Dried*

This method is cost-effective, easy to access, and works great if you live in a dry environment. But it isn't foolproof, and I wouldn't recommend it for those who live in humid environments. However, even after the drying process is complete, there is a chance that your mushrooms may still contain some moisture in the middle, therefore I normally use it to give my harvest a few extra days of shelf-life.

Using the same method you used during the pre-drying step, you will now lay your mushrooms down on kitchen paper or a fresh towel in front of a fan, but make sure none of them are touching one another, in an environment with relative humidity below 55%. The room you place the mushrooms in should also be well-ventilated, and the fan needs to be positioned in a way that allows it to blow air over the mushrooms. If you have a heater, a fireplace, and a black or dark towel, put the mushrooms as close to the heating elements while drying for better results. Place new layers of kitchen paper under the mushrooms every day. Continue this method until most of the moisture is drawn out. You will check on them frequently and once they become rigid and snap under pressure, they are ready.

## *Desiccant*

Desiccant has the ability to remove the remaining moisture from your mushrooms. You can find desiccants like silica gel in your medicine bottles. It's used to prevent moisture from damaging the medicine, increasing its shelf life. You can buy them online. Using a container that can be sealed until it's airtight, place the silica gel packets in a layer on the bottom before covering them in a layer of paper towels. Place a wire rack over the silica gel layer and place your mushrooms on the rack. It's important that your mushrooms **never** touch the silica gel as it isn't safe for ingestion. Seal the container properly and store it in a cool, dark environment. You will still need to check on your mushrooms regularly and once they become brittle, they are ready to be stored in a fresh, but airtight, container.

## Sushi Mat

Place your paper towels in a well-ventilated area with direct sunlight. Put the sushi mat on top of the paper towels. Spread out your magic mushrooms across the mat, making sure there is enough space in between each one. Leave your mushrooms to dry. It roughly takes 24 hours for your shrooms to dry properly, but make sure they are bone dry. Their stems should snap when you bend them!

I don't recommend drying your mushrooms in the oven because of the lack of ventilation, and putting them in an area with static, hot air will cook them instead of drying them. Some users still do it by leaving the oven door open and lifting them from the bottom, keeping the temperature low. This might work but I have never tried it.

There is no real-time limit to how long it will take to dry your batch. Remember, variables such as environment, equipment used, the size of the bunch, and how big the specimens are, all play a role. Instead, identify specific trademarks, including whether the stem snaps when you break it. Is the cap brittle and does it turn to powder if you continue to break it down? As soon as you've effectively dried them, you'll want to make sure you store the mushrooms correctly.

# Long-Term Storage

Dried mushrooms can last for over a year if stored properly. Your mushrooms must not come into contact with oxygen, heat, and ultraviolet (UV) radiation during storage for effective preservation. I wouldn't recommend cold storing either, nor storing long-term in powder form, as a study aiming to determine the stability of tryptamines found that powdered mushrooms and cold exposure resulted in a decrease in their potency at a faster rate (Theibert, 2021). They should be perfectly fine if you store them at room temperature in an airtight container placed in a dark place.

## *Capsules*

Capsules allow you to measure out the correct amount, saving you time. A clever method is to keep your dried mushrooms intact and only turn them into powder form when you prepare a week's dose. The less you fiddle with your dried mushrooms the better. Once your capsules are filled, place them in a container that has a desiccant, just like the tablets in a medicine bottle.

## Mason Jars

You can buy mason jars at your local grocery store, just be sure to clean and sterilize them before use. It's probably one of the easier methods to store your mushrooms and allows them to last for up to 12 months in a cool, dry, and dark environment. Write the date of initial storage on your jar so you can keep track of when you first filled it, and ensure the jar is sealed properly.

## Ziploc Bags

Just like mason jars, you can buy ziploc bags meant for food storage at your local supermarket. They are easy to access and cost-effective. After placing your mushrooms in the bag, squeeze out all the air from the bag—without crushing your mushrooms—and seal it. Check the bag for any excess air or holes that could allow oxygen and moisture in. Some microdosers will then zip lock the bag and place it in a mason jar to ensure no air or moisture can get in. You will store the bag containing your mushrooms in a cool, dark, and dry area. Additionally, you can add a silica gel packet in the ziplock bag or mason jar, separated from the mushrooms with a piece of paper towel.

# Key Takeaways

- Psilocybin concentration will differ among strains and species of mushroom, as well as between specimens of the same strain.

- Always start with the smallest dose possible and work up incrementally until you reach your optimal dose.

- Potency varies among species, so if you change your strain, be mindful that you may need to readjust your dose.

- Psilocybin can be sourced from mushrooms you foraged or grew yourself.

- Drying mushrooms makes it easier to weigh out your optimal dose and to preserve your batch.

- Dried mushrooms should be stored whole in an airtight container that is placed in a cool, dry, and dark place.

You now have a good foundation of microdosing knowledge, as well as how to source, prepare, and store your mushrooms successfully. In Chapter 4, we will discuss taking your first dose and the necessary protocols to keep in mind.

# Chapter 4: Ready to Get Started

While you now have a good knowledge base, you first need to decide which microdosing protocol you will use before taking your first dose. Creating a predetermined schedule that details when you will take your dose, how often you will microdose, and whether you will "stack" your psilocybin with other vitamins or mushrooms is known as your "microdosing protocol." This protocol helps you figure out how to take enough doses of psilocybin to experience the benefits you are looking to experience, while avoiding building up a tolerance. It also helps you maintain the healthy effects of psilocybin microdosing.

I will discuss the best microdosing protocols so you can decide which one you want to use. Using the "best microdosing practices," discussed later in the chapter, can help you record, track, and reflect on your experience so you can get the most out of it. Before settling on a single protocol, I would suggest trying each one for a full cycle of one month. You can then reflect on your experience and compare how you felt before, during, and after starting it. This will allow you to decide whether you want to try a different microdosing protocol, stick with your current one, or even create one that suits your needs better.

Regardless of the protocol you decide to use, you have to remain consistent, measured, and pay close attention throughout. Being able to track your journey allows you to notice whether you have made any progress, determine if your dose is right, and ensure you don't build up a tolerance to psilocybin. Remember that everyone's microdosing experience is unique, so the information you are able to gather using a specific protocol is the best way to help you decide how to move forward and improve your experience. It also helps you learn how to identify when you need to take a break and how often, or if you need to change the type of protocol you use.

## Microdosing Protocols

Various microdosing protocols exist; however, each protocol is designed with a specific aim in mind. The Fadiman protocol was designed for beginners and the nightcap protocol designed for those hoping to sleep better. Microdosing protocols aren't difficult to practice, but they require you to remain vigilant so you can record your journey—which I'll discuss in the section on journaling. Take notice of how you feel physically and mentally, and reflect on your experience so you can see where you can improve and what needs to be changed. Although, many of the protocols assume that the dose of psilocybin you are using is your optimal dose. Finding this dose may take some trial and error, but you can start out by using the Fadiman protocol to help you figure it out because it was designed for those who are new to microdosing. I would recommend you take your microdose in the morning, to start, and potentially avoid insomnia. If you feel fatigue, you might need to switch the intake to bedtime.

## Fadiman Protocol

This protocol was designed by Dr. James Fadiman, also known as the "Father of Microdosing," a psychologist and authority on psychedelics. His protocol is intended to help those who are new to microdosing. In other words, his schedule is great for beginners; hence, it has a second name, the "beginner's protocol." By using this schedule, you will be able to clearly differentiate between your microdosing and non-microdosing days. This gives you a good foundation for understanding how your current dose of psilocybin affects you, and whether you are experiencing any of the benefits you were aiming for. It also helps you determine if your dose is too high or low. This protocol is quite simple and assumes a four-day cycle followed for eight weeks.

- **Day 1:** You will take your first dose of psilocybin.

- **Day 2:** Often called the "transition day" or "afterglow day," you will experience the residual effects of your dose from the previous day.

- **Day 3:** Your body's systems will return to their regular levels of homeostasis, but these levels will look different for everyone. Microdosing effects typically last up to 48h, so it is the third day when you should be back to normal and notice some differences.

- **Day 4:** The second dose of psilocybin will be taken. Second cycle starts.

This cycle will be continued for four to eight weeks, with a reset period that takes the form of two to four weeks of rest—where you don't take any doses of psilocybin. This prevents you from building up tolerance.

### *Stamets Protocol*

Developed by mycologist Paul Stamets, this protocol was developed and tested to create a slightly more intense microdosing schedule. As such, it's ideal for medium to advanced levels of microdosers, and it may not be ideal for beginners. Stamets recommends using what is called "stacking" to intensify the positive effects of psilocybin on your brain health. I will discuss the "Stamets Stack" under "Synergic Stacking," but essentially Stamets recommends combining your psilocybin dose with lion's mane (a medicinal mushroom) and niacin (also known as vitamin B3). Stamets' protocol has a more intense schedule with four days of dosing and three days of rest.

- **Day 1 to 4:** You will dose using the Stamets Stack, also called "stacking days."

- **Day 5 to 7:** Transition days where you experience the residual effects of stacking.

- **Day 8 to 11:** Stacking days.

- **Day 12 to 14:** Transition days.

This cycle is repeated during four weeks, with two to four weeks of rest to reset your system.

### *Institute Protocol*

Designed by the Microdosing Institute, an educational platform that aims to share research on microdosing topics, this protocol is based on anecdotal evidence and modern science that has allowed the Institute to create a community of experts and microdosers. While their protocol is more effective when you are looking at microdosing for medical purposes, this schedule is useful if you experience social anxiety, depression, ADHD, migraines, or cluster headaches. With this protocol, you will take your dose of psilocybin every second day. If you are considering this protocol for managing any medical or mental health condition, please do not hesitate to consult your healthcare provider. This protocol uses the following schedule

- **Day 1:** Take your first dose of psilocybin.

- **Day 2:** Transition day.

- **Day 3:** Take your second dose of psilocybin.

- **Day 4:** Transition day.

This cycle will be continued for four to eight weeks, with an interrupted period of two to four weeks.

## Nightcap Protocol

Microdosers usually use this schedule when they experience fatigue after their intake. This fatigue can be managed better before bedtime, giving a better rest along with more vivid dreams, according to the reports. The nightcap protocol involves taking your dose every second day, at least one hour before going to bed. You can use one of two options when using this protocol.

**Option 1**
The Microdosing Institute Protocol remains the same, except you take your dose at night, one hour before bed:

- **Night 1:** Take your first dose of psilocybin.

- **Night 2:** Transition night, meaning you will experience the residual effects of your dose from the previous evening.

- **Night 3:** Take your second dose of psilocybin.

- **Night 4:** Your second transition night.

This cycle will be repeated for four to eight weeks, with two to four weeks of rest.

## Option 2

The Fadiman Protocol remains the same, except you take your dose at night:

- **Night 1:** Take your first dose of psilocybin.

- **Night 2:** Transition night where you experience the residual effects of your dose from the evening before.

- **Night 3:** A regular evening where you don't take any psilocybin and your body should return to normal levels.

- **Night 4:** Take your second dose of psilocybin.

This cycle will be repeated for four to eight weeks, with two to four weeks of rest.

### *Intuitive Microdosing*

You may find that after using one of the previous protocols for a while, you begin taking a more intuitive approach to microdosing. Using a set schedule first can teach you how to actively notice how psilocybin affects you and how you feel, and helps you decide when you should keep going, rest, or stop. Although intuitive microdosing has one set rule: Avoid microdosing every day and take periodic breaks to prevent your tolerance from building up.

# Synergic Stackings

Many people start microdosing to improve their health. Synergic stacking is a method used by microdosers to enhance the benefits they are looking to experience. Stacking is when a person combines psilocybin with another substance, but you have to be careful. You can't decide to create your own stack without understanding how psilocybin could interact with that specific substance. I will cover the three main synergic stackings that exist to boost your health and the positive effects of psilocybin.

## *Psilocybin With Lion's Mane and Niacin (Stamets' Stack)*

I briefly mentioned this stack under Stamets' Protocol because his schedule combines two mushrooms—one containing psilocybin, and the lion's mane mushroom—with vitamin B3 to create a synergetic combination. This stack is based on the idea that lion's mane enhances cognitive functioning and psilocybin's ability to trigger neurogenesis, boosting its long-term effects. Niacin, a B3 vitamin, increases vasodilation and flushing of the skin, and it may be able to transport psilocybin and lion's mane across your blood-brain barrier so it can distribute these molecules more effectively.

This stack could be used to help you increase your sense of well-being, reduce your anxiety and irritability, boost your immune system, enhance your cognitive functions, and increase your creativity levels. According to Stamets, each substance is measured out per 154.32 lb (70 kg) of the user's weight. He recommends that the mushroom containing psilocybin (of 0.1 g to 0.2 g, and up to 0.5 g if tolerance is built) and lion's mane (500 mg to 1,000 mg) be taken 20 minutes before the niacin (50 mg to 200 mg) (Microdosing Institute, 2020). Additionally, Stamets suggests using the mycelium from the lion's mane (*Hericium erinaceus*) instead of the mushroom (fruiting body).

Breaks are important for preventing your tolerance to psilocybin from building up, but it is safe for you to keep taking lion's mane and niacin during these breaks. Stacking works exactly like finding your optimal dose of psilocybin. You have to start with the lowest dose possible (particularly with niacin, whose dose is significantly higher than the daily recommended value) and slowly work your way up until you reach your optimal dose. If you choose the Stamets Protocol, you can first dose psilocybin only for a few weeks. Once you add the other components, you can see if the results are different.

Please take note that some individuals may be disqualified from taking niacin, as well as other substances. Please do your own research and consult with your healthcare provider to ensure that you can safely consume these substances.

## Psilocybin With Magnesium

Our bodies need magnesium to carry out metabolic processes. It also plays an important role in maintaining brain health, regulating muscle contractions, improving sleep, managing migraines, and reducing symptoms of depression. Magnesium itself is a powerful muscle relaxer, so consider following the Nightcap Protol when using this stack. The daily recommended intake for women is 310 mg to 320 mg, while men need 400 mg to 420 mg of magnesium (Raman, 2018). Combining magnesium with your psilocybin dose may have the potential to enhance psilocybin's ability to increase neurogenesis, improve brain health and functioning, manage migraines, and increase your energy levels.

## Psilocybin with Cordyceps

*Ophiocordyceps sinensis* is a type of mushroom that has the ability to improve a person's physical performance and stimulate the immune system, with a long history of use in traditional Chinese medicine. When combined with psilocybin, it may be able to boost psilocybin's ability to increase your energy levels and manage symptoms related to cancer, like depression. However, it has mainly been used by those who do sports due to its energizing effects. If you have a sleep disorder, struggle with inflammatory diseases, or acute infections, you should not use this stack.

There are many other synergetic combinations that can enhance psilocybin's positive attributes, like the Institute stack which combines psilocybin, cordyceps mushrooms, and vitamin B12. Some users have stacked vitamin D and microdosing, or CBD and microdosing. Feel free to find out more about other stackings.

# Best Microdosing Practices

While stacking is a great way to enhance psilocybin's positive attributes, you can actively take part in activities like meditation and journaling to get the most out of each dose of psilocybin you take. I have included some of the practices commonly used by experienced microdosers below.

## *Journaling*

Journaling is one of the best microdosing practices, and I would recommend that you use this practice regardless of your experience. Journaling helps you keep a record of each microdosing session. Each journal entry will include the date, time, and exact dosage of psilocybin you took. You should also record how your thoughts, behaviors, mood, creativity, and energy levels changed before, during, and after taking your dose. You should also take note of how you feel on the transition days, including how you slept. It's vital that you also record any undesirable effects or side effects as it will help you understand how psilocybin impacts you and whether your dose is right.

Journaling is a great way to help you process your emotions, create clear intentions, and make adjustments to your schedule and how you practice microdosing. I will be leaving my own journal design at the end of the book that you can refer to and use as a template to create your own microdosing journal. Follow up every month and see the results and trends as I designed them.

### Meditation

While microdosing, psilocybin can trigger feelings of anxiety due to its stimulating effects. Practices like meditation are a great way to help you stay calm and find clarity when your anxiety levels increase. Meditation also helps you practice introspection, take notice of your thoughts and how your body feels, as well as improving your brain's ability to grow and stay healthy. As such, meditation can enhance psilocybin's ability to improve your brain health and functioning. You don't have to meditate for hours. Start small with five minutes and slowly increase it until you find the practice that works for you. You could even practice mindfulness meditation, or use a mantra.

## *Music or Dancing*

This is a form of self-care that caters to your mental health. It's a great way to feel and embrace your emotions while also letting go of them through healthy behaviors like dancing. Create different playlists of your favorite music that can induce desirable moods—happy, nostalgic, on top of the world, confident, etc.—that you can swap between. That way, if you feel sad, angry, or frustrated on the day you are supposed to take your dose of psilocybin, you can lift your mood using music and dancing (this is a type of anchoring known as neurolinguistic programming, or NLP). You can even use this method to help you cope with intense emotions and anxiety.

## *Exercise*

Microdosing with psilocybin can boost your energy levels and awareness of your body. Take advantage of this and plan some exercises that you enjoy when you take your dose of psilocybin. Yoga and hiking are both great for getting your body moving, while also benefiting your mind. Hiking gives you another benefit by getting you out in nature so you can spend time in the fresh air.

## *Stimulate Your Thoughts, Feelings, and Emotions*

Psilocybin can increase your creativity, boost your productivity and ability to focus, and even help you solve problems. If you find that psilocybin has a positive effect on your mind in this way, you can work on stimulating your thoughts, feelings, and emotions using different techniques like writing, painting, going hiking and immersing yourself in nature, or even working on mentally demanding tasks or projects.

You may even find that there are practices I haven't mentioned here that work for you, like exercising, practicing yoga, or decluttering and organizing your spaces. Additionally, you might want to check shinrin-yoku or forest bathing, as nature and psilocybin are typically a great combination. Try them out and incorporate them into your microdosing protocol so you can get the most out of each dose and improve your health and well-being.

## Key Takeaways

- Microdosing protocols aim to help you experience the benefits of psilocybin without building up a tolerance.

- The protocol you choose should suit your needs and lifestyle.

- Stacking can help you enhance psilocybin's positive effects.

- Include different practices in your routine that can allow you to get the most out of your microdosing journey.

- Journaling is the best way to record your experience, identify where you can improve, note any unwanted side effects, and reflect on your experience.

During your microdosing cycle, you may notice some unwanted side effects. There is a difference between the effects that can accompany a psychedelic trip and the side effects that are harmful to your health. While you now know how to microdose safely with psilocybin, it's a good idea for you to understand possible side effects, and whether you should avoid psilocybin microdosing due to health issues or different medications. I have briefly discussed this topic in previous chapters, but we will go into detail in Chapter 5.

# Chapter 5: Possible Adverse or Common Side Effects

*You wouldn't go hiking in the Himalaya Mountains without any preparation. Well, this is a journey. These are sacraments and medicines that should be treated with respect, and caution.* –Paul Stamets

Microdosing with magic mushrooms is a relatively safe practice for most individuals; however, psilocybin does have minor side effects. Although they normally occur when you take higher doses of psilocybin or don't take any breaks between them, are currently taking medication or mixing psilocybin with other substances, or you have a pre-existing health condition.

Remember, most of the information we have on psilocybin has been obtained through anecdotal reports and psilocybin administered in a controlled, clinical environment with the guidance and supervision of qualified medical professionals. You don't have any type of support when you are taking psilocybin at home, so even though psilocybin is safe to use, you can't be certain how it will affect you until you take your first dose. But you can minimize your risk of possible side effects by educating yourself.

# Who Is Disqualified From Microdosing?

While microdosing with psilocybin can provide you with a number of benefits, there are a few reports of unwanted side effects for those with certain medical conditions and mental disorders. Many of the studies conducted to understand the risks of psilocybin focused on the use of high doses that were commonly used by individuals aiming to experience a psychedelic trip. However, psilocybin itself is actually quite safe to microdose with—when used correctly—and has been classified as one of the safer substances to use when compared to weed, other psychedelics like MDMA, and alcohol.

Because we currently don't know the exact effects of microdosing psilocybin on a host of medical and mental health disorders, especially in the long-term, you should always proceed with caution and consult with your healthcare provider. In general, you should avoid microdosing with psilocybin if you

- are pregnant or breastfeeding (James Fadiman asserts that is safe to breastfeed if you wait at least 6 hours after consumption)

- are taking medications that could trigger a negative interaction, especially antidepressants, Tramadol, or lithium carbonate medicine

- have psychosis or a family history of psychosis, including schizophrenia

- struggle with paranoia

- have recently ingested alcohol or other drugs

- have bipolar disorder, including a family history

- have heart disease

- have abnormal liver functions

- experience epilepsy

- have other conditions that have not yet been identified (or specified here) as being triggered by, or interact badly with, psilocybin

You need to be aware of possible issues you could face so that you can sufficiently prepare yourself before deciding whether you want to microdose with psilocybin or not.

I would recommend that if you find yourself in any of the disqualifying circumstances mentioned in the book—and even other ones not mentioned here—or suspect you have a predisposition to them, or to any other that can be contraindicated, that you first speak with your medical provider before taking your first dose of psilocybin.

## Bipolar Disorder

While psilocybin has the potential to treat depression, those with bipolar disorder may be at risk of experiencing adverse effects when microdosing with psilocybin. We don't have much information on how psilocybin could affect this disorder because individuals with bipolar disorder are normally excluded from clinical trials due to fears of aggravating their condition or triggering manic episodes. One study focusing on the safe administration of psilocybin—under clinical conditions—to treat bipolar disorder found that the use of psilocybin requires caution because 17 cases suggested there was a risk of a manic episode being triggered (Jones, 2021).

## Psychotic Disorder

If you have a family history of psychotic disorders, are at risk of developing one, or currently have one, you have to be cautious about using psychedelic substances altogether. While studies have mainly been conducted using higher doses of psilocybin, research has found that those with psychotic disorders could experience a prolonged psychotic reaction that triggers overwhelming feelings of fear, anxiety, and confusion (Johnson and Griffiths, 2017). This could be dangerous to your health and is one of the reasons why those with psychotic disorders are normally excluded from clinical studies.

## Heart Problems

There are concerns that microdosing with psilocybin could worsen or negatively affect heart conditions. One study that wanted to better understand how psilocybin could affect depression in individuals with heart disease found that under controlled conditions, it could be safely used; however, researchers did warn that higher doses may be harmful (Nkadimeng et al., 2020).

Additionally, there is a theory regarding valvular heart disease (VHD)—which causes weakness, shortness of breath, and sudden cardiac death—that believes medications that have a tendency to bind with the serotonin 2B receptor (5HT2B) may trigger this disease. As psilocybin has an affinity for binding with the 5HT2B receptor, there is concern that it may cause VHD if you microdose with psilocybin in the long term (Thomas, 2022).

## Medications and Possible Drug Interactions

We don't have a lot of information regarding how psilocybin interacts with other substances and medications. Most of what we know is based on the experiences of those who have been microdosing with psilocybin and the few clinical trials that have been conducted. In general, you should avoid combining any medications (mood stabilizers, anxiolytic or antipsychotic medication, antidepressants, psychostimulants, or painkillers), especially if they are psychoactive—like antidepressants, Xanax, and Adderall—as they work on your serotonin system. Psilocybin (active metabolite psilocin) is a serotonin agonist, so when these medications interact with psilocybin, you could experience adverse side effects.

If you are currently taking any medications or supplements, you should first speak with your medical provider to determine how psilocybin could interact with them, and whether you should slowly phase out (under their guidance) your current medications so you can start microdosing. You can't just suddenly stop your medications and start microdosing with psilocybin. This could also trigger a negative interaction as your medications may still be in your bloodstream. When combined with psilocybin, these substances could trigger adverse effects. It is always best to play it safe and avoid mixing substances together when you can't be certain how you will react. However, if you and your healthcare provider find that you can safely microdose with psilocybin, you may still find that you experience some minor side effects.

# Possible Side Effects

Everyone has a different microdosing experience. While we aren't yet aware of the long-term effects of microdosing with psychedelics like psilocybin, it's a good idea for you to understand what side effects you may experience with psilocybin so you can expect them. This decreases the risk of a bad microdosing experience (which is rare in the first place). How you experience each microdosing session will depend on your unique reaction to psilocybin and your state of mind at that moment. In general, you should be in a good headspace, feel calm, and be comfortable in the environment you are taking any dose of psilocybin, as you can't predict the outcomes beforehand. Many side effects are dose-dependent, and most of the significant or intense ones not yet mentioned, like unintended hallucinations, come from consuming high doses. The side effects you can experience when you take a microdose (typically a bit exceeded) can include but are not limited to

- nausea

- tingling sensations

- a mild upset stomach

- dilated pupils

- "trails" in the vision field of colorblind users

- visual alterations or distortions

- headaches

- impaired concentration

- hyperactivity

- lack of coordination

- insomnia

- drowsiness

- anxiety

- paranoia

- tinnitus

- dry mouth

- loss of appetite

- sweating

## *Sleep*

Psilocybin can affect your ability to get a good night's rest. Its antidepressant potential, related to psilocybin's ability to act as a serotonin agonist, means it could make it harder for you to fall asleep and sleep well. A study aiming to understand how psilocybin could affect sleep administered a placebo or psilocybin, during two different administration sessions, to 20 volunteers.

Their study found that psilocybin can delay the onset of REM sleep, acting in a manner that was similar to classical antidepressants, and promoting slow-wave activity (SWA) that occurs before REM sleep (Dudysová et al., 2020).

## *Hallucinogen Persisting Perception Disorder (HPPD)*

After using a psychedelic substance, normally at higher dosages, a person could experience lingering and distressing changes to how they perceive themselves and their surroundings. These changes result in a disorder known as "hallucinogen persisting perception disorder (HPPD)." Essentially, an individual experiences persisting changes in their perception, hallucinations, or episodic flashbacks that would normally occur when a person is under the influence of higher doses of psychedelic substances like LSD or psilocybin. Persisting changes to how a person perceives themselves and reality can trigger a distressed state that could be harmful to their health.

Currently, no deaths, injuries, or illnesses have been specifically linked to the safe use of mushrooms containing psilocybin. Many of the deaths associated with mushrooms occur when a person confuses or misidentifies the mushroom they wish to use with a more deadly species that is not safe for consumption in any way. Microdosing also becomes risky when a person takes high doses of psilocybin, especially if this is a frequent occurrence. When this happens in an unsafe or uncontrolled environment, a person may have an adverse psychological reaction that is often referred to as a "bad trip."

Other side effects like "wood lover paralysis" can occur when you take higher doses intended to trip. For instance, with a "heroic dose," users might fall into a psychosis where they are completely detached from reality, known as "ego death," which can be very frightening if it is not expected. This doesn't mean higher doses are not beneficial for other treatments, but rather that microdosing is our main focus topic in this book. Our previous book *Psilocybin Mushrooms: 3 in 1: How to Grow Psychedelic Magic Mushrooms, Safe Use and Basic Mushroom Identification* goes into detail about all this in the "Safe Use" section.

### Should You Consult Your Healthcare Provider?

Legality issues mean we currently don't have enough information on exactly how psilocybin interacts with medications or certain medical conditions. Despite psilocybin being safe to use, with minimal risks, it would be best to consult with your healthcare provider first. This may be scary, but it's important because an unknown, current, or prior medical condition and prescription medication could increase the risk of adverse effects when microdosing with psilocybin.

Psychosis, schizophrenia, and bipolar disorder are just a few of the possible medical conditions that could disqualify you from microdosing. You may have a family history of such disorders, or you might not be aware that you are predisposed to them. Medical professionals may not always have the training or experience to guide you on the safe use of psilocybin, but they can help you ensure you aren't at risk of triggering a medical condition or risking your safety or health. They may even be able to refer you to a medical professional who does have more knowledge. And I encourage you to take this guide with you.

If your regular general practitioner doesn't want to give you an answer or is unable to help you, do your research about the professionals who could answer your questions and assist you in ensuring you have a safe and pleasant experience with psychedelics. Speaking with your fellow microdosers is also a good idea because someone may be able to help you find answers to questions or even a professional who could help you. Many people choose to microdose with psilocybin to improve their health, so don't add to your risk by avoiding a conversation with someone who could help you improve your microdosing experience.

# Key Takeaways

- Microdosing with psilocybin is safe as long as you take the necessary precautions and heed the microdosing guidelines.

- Underlying medical conditions, a history of psychosis, and medications could disqualify you from microdosing.

- Microdosing looks different for everyone and you will have a unique reaction to psilocybin depending on the dose.

- Consult your healthcare provider to better understand how microdosing with psilocybin could affect you.

- Medical providers may be able to refer you to someone with more expertise on this topic.

- Don't risk your health to avoid a conversation.

You may or may not experience side effects while microdosing, but it's safer to be prepared. However, taking high doses or mixing psilocybin with other substances aren't the only risks of using it for microdosing. Psilocybin faces a number of legal challenges that can make it hard for microdosers to safely and legally obtain this substance. How does this affect you? Let's discuss it.

# Chapter 6: Legality

Psilocybin and psilocin fall into the Class A category of most illegal drugs in the United Kingdom (UK) and are categorized under federal law as Schedule I controlled substances in the US. They're considered to be drugs with a high potential for abuse, and no current medical use, according to the Comprehensive Drug Abuse Prevention and Control Act.

Certain states or cities have "decriminalized" them, but that does not exempt you entirely from legal consequences. The onus is on you to do the research and find out what laws apply to you and what that means for your microdosing experience, especially if you are going to share these substances with others.

## Decriminalization Versus Legalization

Although a state may decriminalize psilocybin, it may remain illegal at a national level. However, you may be allowed to possess a certain amount of psilocybin, for personal use, under specific circumstances. If you are found in possession of psilocybin—either exceeding the amount, carrying it in public, or not under the exemption criteria—you may be subject to a fine or similar legal penalties, with major consequences generally off the table.

Meanwhile, legalization means that psilocybin—which was originally considered "illegal" in a specific state—is now classified as legal. But just like with decriminalization, there are certain restrictions and requirements in place for a person to be able to legally possess and consume any mushroom containing psilocybin. Either way, psilocybin remains largely illegal to possess and use, and you cannot distribute this substance either, making it almost impossible for you to find reliable, safe, and legal suppliers. But there are a few countries where psilocybin is legal.

### *Where Is Psilocybin Legal?*

Every country has different laws relating to the legality and decriminalization of psilocybin mushrooms. While I will provide you with a brief overview, you will have to research your country's and state's laws to determine whether you can legally buy, cultivate, possess, or use mushrooms containing psilocybin.

Canada considers it illegal to have dried magic mushrooms in your possession, but you can buy the spores of these mushrooms and buy grow kits. Some Canadian businesses also sell magic mushroom products because their laws are quite relaxed. The Netherlands are another country where magic mushrooms are technically illegal, but their laws have loopholes that allow certain businesses to legally sell magic truffles, which also contain psilocybin. They are also home to a number of psychedelic retreats.

Countries like Brazil have relaxed laws relating to magic mushrooms, the fungal body containing psilocybin is legal; however, the substance itself is considered illegal. In Mexico these mushrooms have been classified as legal for the indigenous people who use magic mushrooms for cultural and spiritual purposes.

Magic mushrooms are completely legal in the Bahamas, Samoa, and Jamaica, the last being particularly known for their psychedelic retreats. These mushrooms have also been officially decriminalized in Austria, but there are certain restrictions pertaining to their legality.

While Spain has decriminalized the possession and consumption of psilocybin mushrooms, it's still illegal to grow or sell them. Portugal has decriminalized possession of all drugs, but if you are caught with them in your possession, you could still face penalties.

As you can see, legalization and decriminalization of magic mushrooms is a complex topic as every countries' laws and culture will view magic mushrooms differently. But the way that laws are separately structured around magic mushrooms and psilocybin means that many people can use loopholes to use psilocybin for medical, spiritual, and even recreational purposes. However, I do not condone or support anyone who uses it in parts of the world where it is against the law to do so. I do, however, realize that illegal drug use will occur, and I believe that responsible and educational information is crucial to keep users safe.

### Magic Mushroom Retreats

Going on a psychedelic mushroom retreat is a great way to get away from a situation where you are not in the right headspace for microdosing. Retreats have been designed to help you use psychedelic substances safely. They aim to guide you on your journey to inner healing and help you understand yourself, address trauma, and reflect on your path in life in a safe and supportive environment. While this substance is illegal in many countries, psychedelic mushroom retreats have been designed in such a way that you can legally consume magic mushrooms. Mexico, and the Netherlands are well-known for their psychedelic mushroom retreats.

# Drug Testing and Other Questions

I would recommend that you first answer all your questions related to microdosing with psilocybin before taking the next step in your journey. While I have answered many of the common questions related to microdosing psilocybin throughout the previous chapters, I will answer a few additional questions below.

## *Can Drug Tests Detect Psilocybin?*

You need a specific and more complex drug testing kit to detect the presence of psilocybin in a person's body because regular drug testing kits don't normally screen for this substance, but if you are microdosing this substance, the levels found in your body will very likely be too low for a positive result, plus psilocybin is rapidly metabolized. However, hair follicle tests can successfully detect the presence of drugs consumed within the previous 90 days, but this type of testing is expensive and, hence, uncommon.

## *How Long Does Psilocybin Stay in Your System?*

Psilocybin can stay in your system from 8 to 24 hours. Although this depends on various factors, including your age, current health status, the dose you took, and other biological characteristics, as they all play a role in how fast you will metabolize psilocybin.

## *Is Microdosing Safe?*

Overall, microdosing with psilocybin is safe as long as you take all the necessary precautions and follow the correct microdosing procedure. You must consider your risk-reward ratio. If you are a healthy individual and there is low risk or no risk, and the rewards you can get are high, stick to your regime.

If you still have questions, please make use of online forums, microdosing communities like the Microdosing Institute, and conduct your own research to answer any other questions you may have.

# Key Takeaways

- Psilocybin has been listed as a Schedule I drug under the Convention on Psychotropic Substances by the United Nations since 1971.

- Legality does change according to a country's unique laws, which are further impacted by the state, province, or region you live in.

- Specific drug tests may detect psilocybin, depending on numerous factors.

- Mushroom spore kits and spores are often sold online legally because they do not contain psilocin or psilocybin.

While I have provided you with a broad understanding of the legal issues surrounding psilocybin in the present, you need to do some research of your own to decide whether you can legally microdose with psilocybin or not. Afterwards, you will have all the knowledge you need to decide how you will begin your microdosing journey.

# Conclusion

Psilocybin has a lot of potential. Learning how to safely microdose with this substance and use it in a way that is unique to your lifestyle is a great first step on your journey to improving your health and well-being. You now have the knowledge you need to better understand psilocybin and its healing potential. Whether you are looking to improve your own health or help someone you care about, this form of alternative medicine may be just what you need to help you live the life you need.

Psilocybin's rich history means that while legality issues may have stunted the type of research that can be conducted, we still have anecdotal evidence of its potential benefits. And these benefits are numerous. Although we don't have a lot of empirical evidence to support psilocybin's potential as an alternative medicine, the clinical studies available are promising, especially in relation to the treatment of depression.

But deciding to microdose with psilocybin is a personal decision. Whatever you choose, you have to ensure you are following microdosing guidelines and taking the necessary precautions. Fortunately, microdosing protocols can be tailored to your unique lifestyle and needs. Take advantage of this and find what works for you. Your microdosing practices may change over time. It's both normal and desirable because as you learn and grow while microdosing, you can become the best version of yourself.

There are few risks associated with microdosing psilocybin, but I encourage you to speak with your healthcare provider to ensure you don't have any underlying medical conditions, or are predisposed to one, that could be triggered or affected by psilocybin. Always do your best to ensure your health and safety when microdosing. This includes understanding how your country's laws and regulations could impact your ability to microdose with psilocybin.

Do your best to stay patient, but you may be lucky enough to start seeing results after your first session of microdosing. Once you start experiencing psilocybin's benefits, you will realize that all of your hard work to get to the point of taking your first dose was worth it.

You have already taken the first step on your journey to microdosing, now it's time to decide if you will take the second step.

# Microdosing Journal

MICRODOSING

*Tracker*

# Journal

One of the best practices when microdosing is to keep a journal to track your journey and find out what is working and what isn't working, so you can adjust. Remember it is advised to start small and adjust with small increases, dropping back the dosage weight when needed. I recommend you start journaling before you even start microdosing, so you can have a reference on how you were feeling before starting. And try to keep objective and be always honest.

Notes for the daily journal:

- Include the date of the last time you took it in "Last Intake".
- BOD stands for "Beginning of Day".
- EOD stands for "End of Day".
- In "Day" include both the day of the week and the day of the month.
- Fill in the drawn boxes with a scale that goes from one to ten, being zero null effect. You can do it later in the day but try to keep doing it at a regular time.
- The reflection/observations section can be completed at the end of the day, or perhaps the next day. It can include changes in your thoughts, behavior, and others.
- The daily benefit score goes from 1 to 100, being the total sum of the factors analyzed on that day.
- In "Form" you can include if the specimen is dry or fresh, as well as the potency or strain you are taking.

Notes for the monthly overview:

- The first graph is intended to illustrate the monthly trend of the overall benefit from your microdosing journey. You will need the daily score tracking for at least a whole month.
- The rest of the graphs can be personalized, you might want to illustrate your monthly trend of creativity, sleep quality, or calmness to reflect your anxiety levels. So, feel free to use it at your convenience.
- The graphs are made following the monthly timeframe, but again feel free to increase or decrease the counting days.

# JOURNAL EXAMPLE

| DAY/TIME | DOSE | FORM | LAST INTAKE |
|---|---|---|---|
| Sat 24th Dec, 9am | 0.15 g | Dry Golden T, 0.63% | Thur 22th Dec, 7am |

GOALS/INTENTIONS *I would love to stop fear from holding me back. I want to enjoy exercising this evening, as I am not very motivated lately…*

FEELINGS BOD *I feel like having more self-compassion for myself than in the previous weeks, I woke up at 8:45 am and I am not guilty of it.*

| | | | |
|---|---|---|---|
| **MOOD** | 9 | NOTES | |
| **COGNITIVE FUNCTIONING** | 7 | NOTES | |
| **CALMNESS** | 9 | NOTES | *I don't feel distressed anymore* |
| **CONCENTRATION** | 7 | NOTES | |
| **FOCUS / PRODUCTIVITY** | 7 | NOTES | *Less procrastination* |
| **ENERGY LEVELS** | 6 | NOTES | |
| **RELATIONAL SKILLS** | 8 | NOTES | *I felt very confident talking to my neighbors today.* |
| **SENSES** | 7 | NOTES | *Was I seeing brighter colors? I appreciated more the music that's for sure.* |
| **SLEEP** | 10 | NOTES | *I slept great and had some lucid dreams (I was in Africa).* |
| **SENSE OF CONNECTION/ INTROSPECTION** | 9 | NOTES | *I loved today's hike; I felt a deep connection with Mother Earth* |
| **DAILY BENEFIT SCORE** | 79 | NOTES | |

# JOURNAL EXAMPLE

*My anxiety is gone.*

*I felt a little bit nervous this morning*

*I didn't have a lot of appetite for breakfast, perhaps I waited too long.*

*I feel strong and proud of myself. I also feel inspired.*

*I went exercising and it was raining, and I didn't care :) And I feel I am forgiving myself...*

# Monthly Overview Example

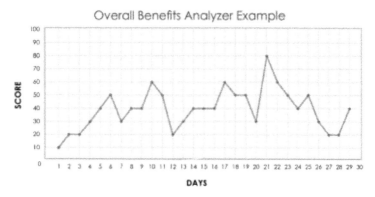

### Overall Benefits Analyzer Example

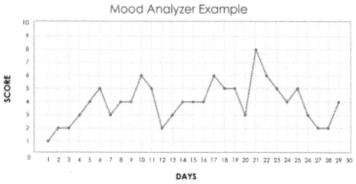

### Mood Analyzer Example

### Clamness Analyzer (Inverted anxiety) Example

| DAY/TIME | DOSE | FORM | LAST INTAKE |
|----------|------|------|-------------|
|          |      |      |             |

GOALS/INTENTIONS

FEELINGS BOD

MOOD ☐ NOTES

COGNITIVE FUNCTIONING ☐ NOTES

CALMNESS ☐ NOTES

CONCENTRATION ☐ NOTES

FOCUS / PRODUCTIVITY ☐ NOTES

ENERGY LEVELS ☐ NOTES

RELATIONAL SKILLS ☐ NOTES

SENSES ☐ NOTES

SLEEP ☐ NOTES

SENSE OF CONNECTION/
INTROSPECTION ☐ NOTES

DAILY BENEFIT SCORE ☐ NOTES

EFFECTS ON HEALTH ISSUES

NEGATIVE EFFECTS

SIDE EFFECTS (AND SEVERITY)

FEELINGS EOD

REFLECTION/OBSERVATIONS

| DAY/TIME | DOSE | FORM | LAST INTAKE |
|----------|------|------|-------------|
|          |      |      |             |

GOALS/INTENTIONS

FEELINGS BOD

MOOD ☐ NOTES

COGNITIVE FUNCTIONING ☐ NOTES

CALMNESS ☐ NOTES

CONCENTRATION ☐ NOTES

FOCUS / PRODUCTIVITY ☐ NOTES

ENERGY LEVELS ☐ NOTES

RELATIONAL SKILLS ☐ NOTES

SENSES ☐ NOTES

SLEEP ☐ NOTES

SENSE OF CONNECTION/
INTROSPECTION ☐ NOTES

DAILY BENEFIT SCORE ☐ NOTES

EFFECTS ON HEALTH ISSUES

NEGATIVE EFFECTS

SIDE EFFECTS (AND SEVERITY)

FEELINGS EOD

REFLECTION/OBSERVATIONS

121

| DAY/TIME | DOSE | FORM | LAST INTAKE |
|----------|------|------|-------------|
|          |      |      |             |

GOALS/INTENTIONS

FEELINGS BOD

MOOD ☐ NOTES

COGNITIVE FUNCTIONING ☐ NOTES

CALMNESS ☐ NOTES

CONCENTRATION ☐ NOTES

FOCUS / PRODUCTIVITY ☐ NOTES

ENERGY LEVELS ☐ NOTES

RELATIONAL SKILLS ☐ NOTES

SENSES ☐ NOTES

SLEEP ☐ NOTES

SENSE OF CONNECTION/
INTROSPECTION ☐ NOTES

DAILY BENEFIT SCORE ☐ NOTES

EFFECTS ON HEALTH ISSUES

NEGATIVE EFFECTS

SIDE EFFECTS (AND SEVERITY)

FEELINGS EOD

REFLECTION/OBSERVATIONS

| DAY/TIME | DOSE | FORM | LAST INTAKE |
|---|---|---|---|

GOALS/INTENTIONS

FEELINGS BOD

MOOD ☐ NOTES

COGNITIVE FUNCTIONING ☐ NOTES

CALMNESS ☐ NOTES

CONCENTRATION ☐ NOTES

FOCUS / PRODUCTIVITY ☐ NOTES

ENERGY LEVELS ☐ NOTES

RELATIONAL SKILLS ☐ NOTES

SENSES ☐ NOTES

SLEEP ☐ NOTES

SENSE OF CONNECTION/ ☐ NOTES
INTROSPECTION

DAILY BENEFIT SCORE ☐ NOTES

EFFECTS ON HEALTH ISSUES

NEGATIVE EFFECTS

SIDE EFFECTS (AND SEVERITY)

FEELINGS EOD

REFLECTION/OBSERVATIONS

| DAY/TIME | DOSE | FORM | LAST INTAKE |
|---|---|---|---|
| | | | |

GOALS/INTENTIONS

FEELINGS BOD

MOOD ☐ NOTES

COGNITIVE FUNCTIONING ☐ NOTES

CALMNESS ☐ NOTES

CONCENTRATION ☐ NOTES

FOCUS / PRODUCTIVITY ☐ NOTES

ENERGY LEVELS ☐ NOTES

RELATIONAL SKILLS ☐ NOTES

SENSES ☐ NOTES

SLEEP ☐ NOTES

SENSE OF CONNECTION/
INTROSPECTION ☐ NOTES

DAILY BENEFIT SCORE ☐ NOTES

EFFECTS ON HEALTH ISSUES

NEGATIVE EFFECTS

SIDE EFFECTS (AND SEVERITY)

FEELINGS EOD

REFLECTION/OBSERVATIONS

| DAY/TIME | DOSE | FORM | LAST INTAKE |
|---|---|---|---|
| | | | |

GOALS/INTENTIONS

FEELINGS BOD

MOOD ☐ NOTES

COGNITIVE FUNCTIONING ☐ NOTES

CALMNESS ☐ NOTES

CONCENTRATION ☐ NOTES

FOCUS / PRODUCTIVITY ☐ NOTES

ENERGY LEVELS ☐ NOTES

RELATIONAL SKILLS ☐ NOTES

SENSES ☐ NOTES

SLEEP ☐ NOTES

SENSE OF CONNECTION/
INTROSPECTION ☐ NOTES

DAILY BENEFIT SCORE ☐ NOTES

| DAY/TIME | DOSE | FORM | LAST INTAKE |
|----------|------|------|-------------|

EFFECTS ON HEALTH ISSUES

NEGATIVE EFFECTS

SIDE EFFECTS (AND SEVERITY)

FEELINGS EOD

REFLECTION/OBSERVATIONS

| DAY/TIME | DOSE | FORM | LAST INTAKE |
|---|---|---|---|
| | | | |

GOALS/INTENTIONS

FEELINGS BOD

| | |
|---|---|
| MOOD | ☐ NOTES |
| COGNITIVE FUNCTIONING | ☐ NOTES |
| CALMNESS | ☐ NOTES |
| CONCENTRATION | ☐ NOTES |
| FOCUS / PRODUCTIVITY | ☐ NOTES |
| ENERGY LEVELS | ☐ NOTES |
| RELATIONAL SKILLS | ☐ NOTES |
| SENSES | ☐ NOTES |
| SLEEP | ☐ NOTES |
| SENSE OF CONNECTION/ INTROSPECTION | ☐ NOTES |
| DAILY BENEFIT SCORE | ☐ NOTES |

EFFECTS ON HEALTH ISSUES

NEGATIVE EFFECTS

SIDE EFFECTS (AND SEVERITY)

FEELINGS EOD

REFLECTION/OBSERVATIONS

| DAY/TIME | DOSE | FORM | LAST INTAKE |
| --- | --- | --- | --- |

GOALS/INTENTIONS

FEELINGS BOD

| | | |
| --- | --- | --- |
| MOOD | ☐ | NOTES |
| COGNITIVE FUNCTIONING | ☐ | NOTES |
| CALMNESS | ☐ | NOTES |
| CONCENTRATION | ☐ | NOTES |
| FOCUS / PRODUCTIVITY | ☐ | NOTES |
| ENERGY LEVELS | ☐ | NOTES |
| RELATIONAL SKILLS | ☐ | NOTES |
| SENSES | ☐ | NOTES |
| SLEEP | ☐ | NOTES |
| SENSE OF CONNECTION/ INTROSPECTION | ☐ | NOTES |
| DAILY BENEFIT SCORE | ☐ | NOTES |

EFFECTS ON HEALTH ISSUES

NEGATIVE EFFECTS

SIDE EFFECTS (AND SEVERITY)

FEELINGS EOD

REFLECTION/OBSERVATIONS

| DAY/TIME | DOSE | FORM | LAST INTAKE |
|----------|------|------|-------------|

GOALS/INTENTIONS

FEELINGS BOD

MOOD ☐ NOTES

COGNITIVE FUNCTIONING ☐ NOTES

CALMNESS ☐ NOTES

CONCENTRATION ☐ NOTES

FOCUS / PRODUCTIVITY ☐ NOTES

ENERGY LEVELS ☐ NOTES

RELATIONAL SKILLS ☐ NOTES

SENSES ☐ NOTES

SLEEP ☐ NOTES

SENSE OF CONNECTION/ ☐ NOTES
INTROSPECTION

DAILY BENEFIT SCORE ☐ NOTES

EFFECTS ON HEALTH ISSUES

NEGATIVE EFFECTS

SIDE EFFECTS (AND SEVERITY)

FEELINGS EOD

REFLECTION/OBSERVATIONS

| DAY/TIME | DOSE | FORM | LAST INTAKE |
|---|---|---|---|

GOALS/INTENTIONS

FEELINGS BOD

MOOD ☐ NOTES

COGNITIVE FUNCTIONING ☐ NOTES

CALMNESS ☐ NOTES

CONCENTRATION ☐ NOTES

FOCUS / PRODUCTIVITY ☐ NOTES

ENERGY LEVELS ☐ NOTES

RELATIONAL SKILLS ☐ NOTES

SENSES ☐ NOTES

SLEEP ☐ NOTES

SENSE OF CONNECTION/ INTROSPECTION ☐ NOTES

DAILY BENEFIT SCORE ☐ NOTES

EFFECTS ON HEALTH ISSUES

NEGATIVE EFFECTS

SIDE EFFECTS (AND SEVERITY)

FEELINGS EOD

REFLECTION/OBSERVATIONS

| DAY/TIME | DOSE | FORM | LAST INTAKE |
|---|---|---|---|

GOALS/INTENTIONS

FEELINGS BOD

MOOD ☐ NOTES

COGNITIVE FUNCTIONING ☐ NOTES

CALMNESS ☐ NOTES

CONCENTRATION ☐ NOTES

FOCUS / PRODUCTIVITY ☐ NOTES

ENERGY LEVELS ☐ NOTES

RELATIONAL SKILLS ☐ NOTES

SENSES ☐ NOTES

SLEEP ☐ NOTES

SENSE OF CONNECTION/ ☐ NOTES
INTROSPECTION

DAILY BENEFIT SCORE ☐ NOTES

EFFECTS ON HEALTH ISSUES

NEGATIVE EFFECTS

SIDE EFFECTS (AND SEVERITY)

FEELINGS EOD

REFLECTION/OBSERVATIONS

139

| DAY/TIME | DOSE | FORM | LAST INTAKE |
|----------|------|------|-------------|
|          |      |      |             |

GOALS/INTENTIONS

FEELINGS BOD

MOOD ☐ NOTES

COGNITIVE FUNCTIONING ☐ NOTES

CALMNESS ☐ NOTES

CONCENTRATION ☐ NOTES

FOCUS / PRODUCTIVITY ☐ NOTES

ENERGY LEVELS ☐ NOTES

RELATIONAL SKILLS ☐ NOTES

SENSES ☐ NOTES

SLEEP ☐ NOTES

SENSE OF CONNECTION/
INTROSPECTION ☐ NOTES

DAILY BENEFIT SCORE ☐ NOTES

EFFECTS ON HEALTH ISSUES

NEGATIVE EFFECTS

SIDE EFFECTS (AND SEVERITY)

FEELINGS EOD

REFLECTION/OBSERVATIONS

| DAY/TIME | DOSE | FORM | LAST INTAKE |
|----------|------|------|-------------|

GOALS/INTENTIONS

FEELINGS BOD

MOOD ☐ NOTES

COGNITIVE FUNCTIONING ☐ NOTES

CALMNESS ☐ NOTES

CONCENTRATION ☐ NOTES

FOCUS / PRODUCTIVITY ☐ NOTES

ENERGY LEVELS ☐ NOTES

RELATIONAL SKILLS ☐ NOTES

SENSES ☐ NOTES

SLEEP ☐ NOTES

SENSE OF CONNECTION/ INTROSPECTION ☐ NOTES

DAILY BENEFIT SCORE ☐ NOTES

EFFECTS ON HEALTH ISSUES

NEGATIVE EFFECTS

SIDE EFFECTS (AND SEVERITY)

FEELINGS EOD

REFLECTION/OBSERVATIONS

| DAY/TIME | DOSE | FORM | LAST INTAKE |
|---|---|---|---|

GOALS/INTENTIONS

FEELINGS BOD

MOOD ☐ NOTES

COGNITIVE FUNCTIONING ☐ NOTES

CALMNESS ☐ NOTES

CONCENTRATION ☐ NOTES

FOCUS / PRODUCTIVITY ☐ NOTES

ENERGY LEVELS ☐ NOTES

RELATIONAL SKILLS ☐ NOTES

SENSES ☐ NOTES

SLEEP ☐ NOTES

SENSE OF CONNECTION/
INTROSPECTION ☐ NOTES

DAILY BENEFIT SCORE ☐ NOTES

EFFECTS ON HEALTH ISSUES

NEGATIVE EFFECTS

SIDE EFFECTS (AND SEVERITY)

FEELINGS EOD

REFLECTION/OBSERVATIONS

| DAY/TIME | DOSE | FORM | LAST INTAKE |
|----------|------|------|-------------|
|          |      |      |             |

GOALS/INTENTIONS

FEELINGS BOD

| | | |
|---|---|---|
| MOOD | ☐ | NOTES |
| COGNITIVE FUNCTIONING | ☐ | NOTES |
| CALMNESS | ☐ | NOTES |
| CONCENTRATION | ☐ | NOTES |
| FOCUS / PRODUCTIVITY | ☐ | NOTES |
| ENERGY LEVELS | ☐ | NOTES |
| RELATIONAL SKILLS | ☐ | NOTES |
| SENSES | ☐ | NOTES |
| SLEEP | ☐ | NOTES |
| SENSE OF CONNECTION/ INTROSPECTION | ☐ | NOTES |
| DAILY BENEFIT SCORE | ☐ | NOTES |

EFFECTS ON HEALTH ISSUES

NEGATIVE EFFECTS

SIDE EFFECTS (AND SEVERITY)

FEELINGS EOD

REFLECTION/OBSERVATIONS

| DAY/TIME | DOSE | FORM | LAST INTAKE |
|----------|------|------|-------------|

GOALS/INTENTIONS

FEELINGS BOD

MOOD ☐ NOTES

COGNITIVE FUNCTIONING ☐ NOTES

CALMNESS ☐ NOTES

CONCENTRATION ☐ NOTES

FOCUS / PRODUCTIVITY ☐ NOTES

ENERGY LEVELS ☐ NOTES

RELATIONAL SKILLS ☐ NOTES

SENSES ☐ NOTES

SLEEP ☐ NOTES

SENSE OF CONNECTION/
INTROSPECTION ☐ NOTES

DAILY BENEFIT SCORE ☐ NOTES

EFFECTS ON HEALTH ISSUES

NEGATIVE EFFECTS

SIDE EFFECTS (AND SEVERITY)

FEELINGS EOD

REFLECTION/OBSERVATIONS

| DAY/TIME | DOSE | FORM | LAST INTAKE |
|----------|------|------|-------------|

GOALS/INTENTIONS

FEELINGS BOD

MOOD ☐ NOTES

COGNITIVE FUNCTIONING ☐ NOTES

CALMNESS ☐ NOTES

CONCENTRATION ☐ NOTES

FOCUS / PRODUCTIVITY ☐ NOTES

ENERGY LEVELS ☐ NOTES

RELATIONAL SKILLS ☐ NOTES

SENSES ☐ NOTES

SLEEP ☐ NOTES

SENSE OF CONNECTION/
INTROSPECTION ☐ NOTES

DAILY BENEFIT SCORE ☐ NOTES

EFFECTS ON HEALTH ISSUES


NEGATIVE EFFECTS


SIDE EFFECTS (AND SEVERITY)


FEELINGS EOD


REFLECTION/OBSERVATIONS

| DAY/TIME | DOSE | FORM | LAST INTAKE |
| --- | --- | --- | --- |
| | | | |

GOALS/INTENTIONS

FEELINGS BOD

MOOD ☐ NOTES

COGNITIVE FUNCTIONING ☐ NOTES

CALMNESS ☐ NOTES

CONCENTRATION ☐ NOTES

FOCUS / PRODUCTIVITY ☐ NOTES

ENERGY LEVELS ☐ NOTES

RELATIONAL SKILLS ☐ NOTES

SENSES ☐ NOTES

SLEEP ☐ NOTES

SENSE OF CONNECTION/
INTROSPECTION ☐ NOTES

DAILY BENEFIT SCORE ☐ NOTES

EFFECTS ON HEALTH ISSUES

NEGATIVE EFFECTS

SIDE EFFECTS (AND SEVERITY)

FEELINGS EOD

REFLECTION/OBSERVATIONS

| DAY/TIME | DOSE | FORM | LAST INTAKE |
|----------|------|------|-------------|

GOALS/INTENTIONS

FEELINGS BOD

MOOD ☐ NOTES

COGNITIVE FUNCTIONING ☐ NOTES

CALMNESS ☐ NOTES

CONCENTRATION ☐ NOTES

FOCUS / PRODUCTIVITY ☐ NOTES

ENERGY LEVELS ☐ NOTES

RELATIONAL SKILLS ☐ NOTES

SENSES ☐ NOTES

SLEEP ☐ NOTES

SENSE OF CONNECTION/
INTROSPECTION ☐ NOTES

DAILY BENEFIT SCORE ☐ NOTES

EFFECTS ON HEALTH ISSUES

NEGATIVE EFFECTS

SIDE EFFECTS (AND SEVERITY)

FEELINGS EOD

REFLECTION/OBSERVATIONS

| DAY/TIME | DOSE | FORM | LAST INTAKE |
|----------|------|------|-------------|

GOALS/INTENTIONS

FEELINGS BOD

| | | |
|---|---|---|
| MOOD | ☐ | NOTES |
| COGNITIVE FUNCTIONING | ☐ | NOTES |
| CALMNESS | ☐ | NOTES |
| CONCENTRATION | ☐ | NOTES |
| FOCUS / PRODUCTIVITY | ☐ | NOTES |
| ENERGY LEVELS | ☐ | NOTES |
| RELATIONAL SKILLS | ☐ | NOTES |
| SENSES | ☐ | NOTES |
| SLEEP | ☐ | NOTES |
| SENSE OF CONNECTION/ INTROSPECTION | ☐ | NOTES |
| DAILY BENEFIT SCORE | ☐ | NOTES |

EFFECTS ON HEALTH ISSUES

NEGATIVE EFFECTS

SIDE EFFECTS (AND SEVERITY)

FEELINGS EOD

REFLECTION/OBSERVATIONS

| DAY/TIME | DOSE | FORM | LAST INTAKE |
|----------|------|------|-------------|
|          |      |      |             |

GOALS/INTENTIONS

FEELINGS BOD

MOOD ☐ NOTES

COGNITIVE FUNCTIONING ☐ NOTES

CALMNESS ☐ NOTES

CONCENTRATION ☐ NOTES

FOCUS / PRODUCTIVITY ☐ NOTES

ENERGY LEVELS ☐ NOTES

RELATIONAL SKILLS ☐ NOTES

SENSES ☐ NOTES

SLEEP ☐ NOTES

SENSE OF CONNECTION/
INTROSPECTION ☐ NOTES

DAILY BENEFIT SCORE ☐ NOTES

EFFECTS ON HEALTH ISSUES

NEGATIVE EFFECTS

SIDE EFFECTS (AND SEVERITY)

FEELINGS EOD

REFLECTION/OBSERVATIONS

| DAY/TIME | DOSE | FORM | LAST INTAKE |
|----------|------|------|-------------|

GOALS/INTENTIONS

FEELINGS BOD

MOOD ☐

COGNITIVE FUNCTIONING ☐

CALMNESS ☐

CONCENTRATION ☐

FOCUS / PRODUCTIVITY ☐

ENERGY LEVELS ☐

RELATIONAL SKILLS ☐

SENSES ☐

SLEEP ☐

SENSE OF CONNECTION/
INTROSPECTION ☐

DAILY BENEFIT SCORE ☐

EFFECTS ON HEALTH ISSUES

NEGATIVE EFFECTS

SIDE EFFECTS (AND SEVERITY)

FEELINGS EOD

REFLECTION/OBSERVATIONS

| DAY/TIME | DOSE | FORM | LAST INTAKE |
|----------|------|------|-------------|

GOALS/INTENTIONS

FEELINGS BOD

MOOD ☐ NOTES

COGNITIVE FUNCTIONING ☐ NOTES

CALMNESS ☐ NOTES

CONCENTRATION ☐ NOTES

FOCUS / PRODUCTIVITY ☐ NOTES

ENERGY LEVELS ☐ NOTES

RELATIONAL SKILLS ☐ NOTES

SENSES ☐ NOTES

SLEEP ☐ NOTES

SENSE OF CONNECTION/
INTROSPECTION ☐ NOTES

DAILY BENEFIT SCORE ☐ NOTES

EFFECTS ON HEALTH ISSUES

NEGATIVE EFFECTS

SIDE EFFECTS (AND SEVERITY)

FEELINGS EOD

REFLECTION/OBSERVATIONS

| DAY/TIME | DOSE | FORM | LAST INTAKE |
|----------|------|------|-------------|

GOALS/INTENTIONS

FEELINGS BOD

| | | |
|---|---|---|
| **MOOD** | ☐ | NOTES |
| **COGNITIVE FUNCTIONING** | ☐ | NOTES |
| **CALMNESS** | ☐ | NOTES |
| **CONCENTRATION** | ☐ | NOTES |
| **FOCUS / PRODUCTIVITY** | ☐ | NOTES |
| **ENERGY LEVELS** | ☐ | NOTES |
| **RELATIONAL SKILLS** | ☐ | NOTES |
| **SENSES** | ☐ | NOTES |
| **SLEEP** | ☐ | NOTES |
| **SENSE OF CONNECTION/ INTROSPECTION** | ☐ | NOTES |
| **DAILY BENEFIT SCORE** | ☐ | NOTES |

EFFECTS ON HEALTH ISSUES

NEGATIVE EFFECTS

SIDE EFFECTS (AND SEVERITY)

FEELINGS EOD

REFLECTION/OBSERVATIONS

| DAY/TIME | DOSE | FORM | LAST INTAKE |
|----------|------|------|-------------|

GOALS/INTENTIONS

FEELINGS BOD

MOOD ☐ NOTES

COGNITIVE FUNCTIONING ☐ NOTES

CALMNESS ☐ NOTES

CONCENTRATION ☐ NOTES

FOCUS / PRODUCTIVITY ☐ NOTES

ENERGY LEVELS ☐ NOTES

RELATIONAL SKILLS ☐ NOTES

SENSES ☐ NOTES

SLEEP ☐ NOTES

SENSE OF CONNECTION/
INTROSPECTION ☐ NOTES

DAILY BENEFIT SCORE ☐ NOTES

EFFECTS ON HEALTH ISSUES


NEGATIVE EFFECTS


SIDE EFFECTS (AND SEVERITY)


FEELINGS EOD


REFLECTION/OBSERVATIONS

| DAY/TIME | DOSE | FORM | LAST INTAKE |
|----------|------|------|-------------|

GOALS/INTENTIONS

FEELINGS BOD

MOOD ☐ NOTES

COGNITIVE FUNCTIONING ☐ NOTES

CALMNESS ☐ NOTES

CONCENTRATION ☐ NOTES

FOCUS / PRODUCTIVITY ☐ NOTES

ENERGY LEVELS ☐ NOTES

RELATIONAL SKILLS ☐ NOTES

SENSES ☐ NOTES

SLEEP ☐ NOTES

SENSE OF CONNECTION/
INTROSPECTION ☐ NOTES

DAILY BENEFIT SCORE ☐ NOTES

EFFECTS ON HEALTH ISSUES

NEGATIVE EFFECTS

SIDE EFFECTS (AND SEVERITY)

FEELINGS EOD

REFLECTION/OBSERVATIONS

| DAY/TIME | DOSE | FORM | LAST INTAKE |
|----------|------|------|-------------|

GOALS/INTENTIONS

FEELINGS BOD

MOOD ☐ NOTES

COGNITIVE FUNCTIONING ☐ NOTES

CALMNESS ☐ NOTES

CONCENTRATION ☐ NOTES

FOCUS / PRODUCTIVITY ☐ NOTES

ENERGY LEVELS ☐ NOTES

RELATIONAL SKILLS ☐ NOTES

SENSES ☐ NOTES

SLEEP ☐ NOTES

SENSE OF CONNECTION/
INTROSPECTION ☐ NOTES

DAILY BENEFIT SCORE ☐ NOTES

EFFECTS ON HEALTH ISSUES

NEGATIVE EFFECTS

SIDE EFFECTS (AND SEVERITY)

FEELINGS EOD

REFLECTION/OBSERVATIONS

| DAY/TIME | DOSE | FORM | LAST INTAKE |
|---|---|---|---|
| | | | |

GOALS/INTENTIONS

FEELINGS BOD

MOOD ☐ NOTES

COGNITIVE FUNCTIONING ☐ NOTES

CALMNESS ☐ NOTES

CONCENTRATION ☐ NOTES

FOCUS / PRODUCTIVITY ☐ NOTES

ENERGY LEVELS ☐ NOTES

RELATIONAL SKILLS ☐ NOTES

SENSES ☐ NOTES

SLEEP ☐ NOTES

SENSE OF CONNECTION/
INTROSPECTION ☐ NOTES

DAILY BENEFIT SCORE ☐ NOTES

EFFECTS ON HEALTH ISSUES

NEGATIVE EFFECTS

SIDE EFFECTS (AND SEVERITY)

FEELINGS EOD

REFLECTION/OBSERVATIONS

| DAY/TIME | DOSE | FORM | LAST INTAKE |
|----------|------|------|-------------|

GOALS/INTENTIONS

FEELINGS BOD

| | | |
|---|---|---|
| MOOD | ☐ | NOTES |
| COGNITIVE FUNCTIONING | ☐ | NOTES |
| CALMNESS | ☐ | NOTES |
| CONCENTRATION | ☐ | NOTES |
| FOCUS / PRODUCTIVITY | ☐ | NOTES |
| ENERGY LEVELS | ☐ | NOTES |
| RELATIONAL SKILLS | ☐ | NOTES |
| SENSES | ☐ | NOTES |
| SLEEP | ☐ | NOTES |
| SENSE OF CONNECTION/ INTROSPECTION | ☐ | NOTES |
| DAILY BENEFIT SCORE | ☐ | NOTES |

EFFECTS ON HEALTH ISSUES

NEGATIVE EFFECTS

SIDE EFFECTS (AND SEVERITY)

FEELINGS EOD

REFLECTION/OBSERVATIONS

# Monthly Overview

### Overall Benefits Analyzer

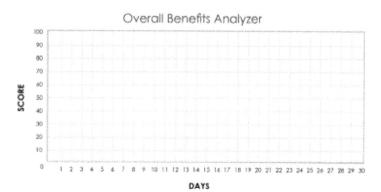

### ———— Analyzer

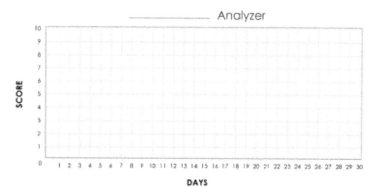

### ———— Analyzer

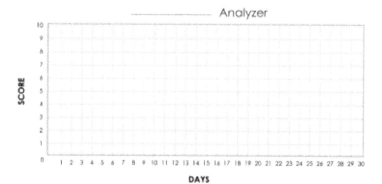

# Monthly Overview

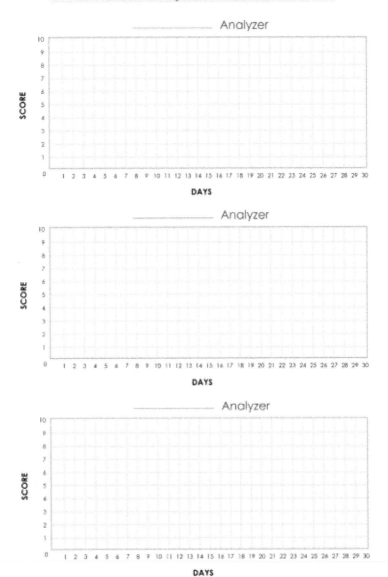

# Monthly Overview

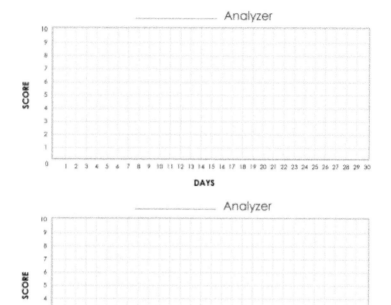

You can download the journal by scanning the next QR code:

The journal is also available for purchase (200 pages):

*"Microdosing Journal: Psilocybin Mushroom Version. Your Healing Journey Starts Here"*

# Dear Reader

I want to personally thank you for choosing this book from among dozens out there, for acquiring an authorized copy of it and supporting my work, and for making it all the way to the end.

If you liked the content, please consider posting a review or rating on Amazon, it would mean a lot to me and it would help others benefit from my work. It is also the best way to support independent writers like myself.

Thank you.

Amazon US

Amazon UK

You can use your respective Amazon market if you don't live in the UK or US.

# References

*A foraging trip: Where do magic mushrooms grow?* (2020, November 19). Reality Sandwich. realitysandwich.com/where-do-magic-mushrooms-grow/

Allitt, M. (2022, December 6). *How to get the most out of your microdosing experience.* Third Wave. thethirdwave.co/get-the-most-out-of-microdosing/

Altschul, D. M. (2020, June 28). What are cognitive functions? *Psychology Today.* psychologytoday.com/us/blog/reverse-causation/202006/what-are-cognitive-functions

Anderson, T., Petranker, R., Christopher, A., Rosenbaum, D., Weissman, C., Dinh-Williams, L.-A., Hui, K., and Hapke, E. (2019). Psychedelic microdosing benefits and challenges: an empirical codebook. *Harm Reduction Journal*, 16(1). doi.org/10.1186/s12954-019-0308-4

Andersson, M., and Kjellgren, A. (2019). Twenty percent better with 20 micrograms? A qualitative study of psychedelic microdosing self-rapports and discussions on YouTube. *Harm Reduction Journal*, 16(1). doi.org/10.1186/s12954-019-0333-3

AstroMonk. (2021, December 4). *Robert Forte PhD—The dark history of psychedelics*. Sacred Geometry International. sacredgeometryinternational.com/robert-forte-the-dark-history-of-psychedelics/

Barlow, C. (2021, August 18). *The top 6 mushroom grow kits (that we've vetted and recommend)*. Third Wave. thethirdwave.co/mushroom-grow-kits/

Bauer, B. E. (2018, December 19). *James Fadiman*. Psychedelic Science Review. psychedelicreview.com/person/james-fadiman/

Butler, O., Willmund, G., Gleich, T., Gallinat, J., Kühn, S., and Zimmermann, P. (2018). Hippocampal gray matter increases following multimodal psychological treatment for combat-related post-traumatic stress disorder. *Brain and Behavior*, 8(5), e00956. doi.org/10.1002/brb3.956

Calder, A. E., and Hasler, G. (2022). Towards an understanding of psychedelic-induced neuroplasticity. *Neuropsychopharmacology*, 48(1), 104–112. doi.org/10.1038/s41386-022-01389-z

Carhart-Harris, R. L., Bolstridge, M., Rucker, J., Day, C. M. J., Erritzoe, D., Kaelen, M., Bloomfield, M., Rickard, J. A., Forbes, B., Feilding, A., Taylor, D., Pilling, S., Curran, V. H., and Nutt, D. J. (2016). Psilocybin with psychological support for treatment-resistant depression: an open-label feasibility study. *The Lancet Psychiatry*, 3(7), 619–627. doi.org/10.1016/s2215-0366(16)30065-7

Carhart-Harris, R. L., Roseman, L., Bolstridge, M., Demetriou, L., Pannekoek, J. N., Wall, M. B., Tanner, M., Kaelen, M., McGonigle, J., Murphy, K., Leech, R., Curran, H. V., and Nutt, D. J. (2017). Psilocybin for treatment-resistant depression: fMRI-measured brain mechanisms. *Scientific Reports*, 7(1). doi.org/10.1038/s41598-017-13282-7

Catlow, B. J., Song, S., Paredes, D. A., Kirstein, C. L., and Sanchez-Ramos, J. (2013). Effects of psilocybin on hippocampal neurogenesis and extinction of trace fear conditioning. *Experimental Brain Research*, 228(4), 481–491. doi.org/10.1007/s00221-013-3579-0

CDC. (2022). *Drug overdose deaths in the U.S. top 100,000 annually.* Centers for Disease Control and Prevention. cdc.gov/nchs/pressroom/nchs_press_releases/2021/20211117.htm

*Company: Vision, values and story.* (2022, September 15). Wesana Health. wesanahealth.com/company/

Compass Pathways. (2022, June 4). COMP360 psilocybin study of 89 healthy participants published in Journal of Psychopharmacology. *Compass News.*

compasspathways.com/comp360-psilocybin-study-89-healthy-participants-journal-of-psychopharmacology/

Cooper, M. (2022, July 21). *Magnesium and microdosing: The perfect pair.* Third Wave. thethirdwave.co/magnesium-microdosing-the-perfect-pair/

Dattani, S., Ritchie, H., and Roser, M. (2021, August 20). *Mental health.* Our World in Data. ourworldindata.org/mental-health

Davis, K. (2021, October 3). What are magic mushrooms and psilocybin? *Medical News Today.* medicalnewstoday.com/articles/308850#effects

DeRose, A. (2022, October 7). *Psilocybin and ADHD: A revolutionary treatment?* Utah Patients Coalition. utahpatients.org/psilocybin-and-adhd-a-revolutionary-treatment/

Dolan, E. W. (2010, January 17). *Psychological and physiological effects of psilocybin.* PsyPost. psypost.org/2010/01/psychological-and-physiological-effects-of-psilocybin-48

Dolan, E. W. (2020, January 20). *Neuroscience study uncovers psilocybin-induced changes in brain connectivity.* PsyPost. psypost.org/2020/01/neuroscience-study-uncovers-psilocybin-induced-changes-in-brain-connectivity-55308

Dorr, A. (2021, December 2). Everything you need to know about microdosing psilocybin. *Mushroom Revival.* mushroomrevival.com/blogs/blog/everything-you-need-to-know-about-microdosing-psilocybin

Dorr, A. (2022). Mushroom Revival Podcast. In *Spotify.* open.spotify.com/show/2bAoRCfGft9upvdZCvho6O

*Double blind randomized controlled trial.* (2016, November 7). PhD Essay. phdessay.com/double-blind-randomized-controlled-trial/

Dudysová, D., Janků, K., Šmotek, M., Saifutdinova, E., Kopřivová, J., Bušková, J., Mander, B. A., Brunovský, M., Zach, P., Korčák, J., Andrashko, V., Viktorinová, M., Tylš, F., Bravermanová, A., Froese, T., Páleníček, T., and Horáček, J. (2020). The effects of daytime psilocybin administration on sleep: Implications for antidepressant action. *Frontiers in Pharmacology,* 11. doi.org/10.3389/fphar.2020.602590

Dumka, G. (2021, January 13). *5 Health benefits of microdosing psilocybin.* DeliveryMeds. deliverymeds.co/5-mental-health-benefits-of-microdosing-psilocybin/

Engle, T. (2022, May 4). *Psilocybin 101: How to store magic mushrooms.* The Bluntness. thebluntness.com/posts/how-to-store-magic-mushrooms

Erritzoe, D., Roseman, L., Nour, M. M., MacLean, K., Kaelen, M., Nutt, D. J., and Carhart-Harris, R. L. (2018). Effects of psilocybin therapy on personality structure. *Acta Psychiatrica Scandinavica*, 138(5), 368–378. doi.org/10.1111/acps.12904

Fewster, E. (2021, September). Psilocybin Retreats - Learn about microdosing retreats - Frshminds. frshminds.com/psilocybin-retreats/

Flanagan, T. W., and Nichols, C. D. (2018). Psychedelics as anti-inflammatory agents. *International Review of Psychiatry*, 30(4), 363–375. doi.org/10.1080/09540261.2018.1481827

Francuski, X. (2020, October 26). *Microdosing magic mushrooms: How to prepare the doses.* Entheonation. entheonation.com/blog/microdosing-magic-mushrooms-prepare-doses/

Fungus Freddy. (2022, October 14). *Where to find psilocybin mushrooms in the wild.* Fungushead. fungushead.com/psilocybin-mushrooms-in-the-wild

Garcia-Romeu, A., Darcy, S., Jackson, H., White, T., and Rosenberg, P. (2021). Psychedelics as novel therapeutics in Alzheimer's disease: Rationale and potential mechanisms. *Disruptive Psychopharmacology*, 287–317. doi.org/10.1007/7854_2021_267

Gillespie, C. (2022). *Comprehensive study finds microdosing boosts mental health*. Very Well Mind. verywellmind.com/most-comprehensive-microdosing-study-to-date-finds-it-improves-mental-health-6265596

Gordon, J., and Bradford, A. (2022, February 8). *Empirical evidence: A definition*. Live Science. livescience.com/21456-empirical-evidence-a-definition.html

Govare, A., and Leroux, E. (2014). Licit and illicit drug use in cluster headache. *Current Pain and Headache Reports*, 18(5). doi.org/10.1007/s11916-014-0413-8

Griffiths, R. R., Johnson, M. W., Carducci, M. A., Umbricht, A., Richards, W. A., Richards, B. D., Cosimano, M. P., and Klinedinst, M. A. (2016). Psilocybin produces substantial and sustained decreases in depression and anxiety in patients with life-threatening cancer: A randomized double-blind trial. *Journal of Psychopharmacology*, 30(12), 1181–1197. doi.org/10.1177/0269881116675513

Griffiths, R. R., Johnson, M. W., Richards, W. A., Richards, B. D., McCann, U., and Jesse, R. (2011). Psilocybin occasioned mystical-type experiences: immediate and persisting dose-related effects. *Psychopharmacology*, 218(4), 649–665. doi.org/10.1007/s00213-011-2358-5

Grob, C. S., Danforth, A. L., Chopra, G. S., Hagerty, M., McKay, C. R., Halberstadt, A. L., and Greer, G. R. (2011). Pilot study of psilocybin treatment for anxiety in patients with advanced-stage cancer. *Archives of General Psychiatry*, 68(1), 71. doi.org/10.1001/archgenpsychiatry.2010.116

Hallifax, J. (2022, May 26). *How to microdose psilocybin according to Paul Stamets: The Stamets Stack*. Psychedelic Spotlight. psychedelicspotlight.com/how-to-microdose-psilocybin-paul-stamets-the-stamets-stack/

Hartney, E. (2022, November 14). *What are psychedelic drugs?* Very Well Mind. verywellmind.com/types-of-psychedelic-drug-22073

Hasler, F., Grimberg, U., Benz, M. A., Huber, T., and Vollenweider, F. X. (2004a). Acute psychological and physiological effects of psilocybin in healthy humans: a double-blind, placebo-controlled dose?effect study. *Psychopharmacology*, 172(2), 145–156. doi.org/10.1007/s00213-003-1640-6

Hasler, F., Grimberg, U., Benz, M. A., Huber, T., and Vollenweider, F. X. (2004b). Acute psychological and physiological effects of psilocybin in healthy humans: a double-blind, placebo-controlled dose?effect study. *Psychopharmacology*, 172(2), 145–156. doi.org/10.1007/s00213-003-1640-6

Hatfield, R. C. (2022, May 6). *Effects of Psilocybin Mushrooms*. American Addiction Centers

DrugAbuse.com drugabuse.com/drugs/hallucinogens/psilocybin-mushrooms/effects-use/

The Healing Co. (2021, February 11). *Will psilocybin help me concentrate?* The Healing Co. Wellness. thehealingcowellness.com/will-psilocybin-help-me-concentrate/

*History of microdosing.* (2020, August 15). Microdosing Institute. microdosinginstitute.com/microdosing-101/history/

Holyanova, M. (2022, October 27). *The strongest magic mushroom species ranked by potency.* Psychedelic Spotlight. psychedelicspotlight.com/the-strongest-magic-mushroom-species-ranked-by-potency/

*Home—psilocybin mushrooms online* USA. (2022, July 15). Psilocybin Mushroom. psilocybinmushroomsonlineusa.com/

*How Long Do Shrooms Stay In Your System?—Psychedelic Mushroom (Psilocybin) Detection Time.* (2019, January 22). Rehab Center. rehabcenter.net/mushrooms/detection-time/

*HPPD: Hallucinogen persisting perception disorder.* (2014). The Psychedelic Society. psychedelicsociety.org.uk/harm-reduction/hppd

Hutten, N. R. P. W., Mason, N. L., Dolder, P. C., and Kuypers, K. P. C. (2019). Self-rated effectiveness of microdosing with psychedelics for mental and physical health problems among microdosers. *Frontiers in Psychiatry,* 10. doi.org/10.3389/fpsyt.2019.00672

*Is microdosing safe? Risks of microdosing.* (2020, August 15). Microdosing Institute. microdosinginstitute.com/microdosing-101/risks-safety-side-effects/

Jastrzebski, M., and Bala, A. (2013). The impact of psilocybin on visual perception and spatial orientation—neuropsychological approach. *Psychiatria Polska,* 47(6). pubmed.ncbi.nlm.nih.gov/25007546/

Johnson, M. W., and Griffiths, R. R. (2017). Potential therapeutic effects of psilocybin. *Neurotherapeutics,* 14(3), 734–740. doi.org/10.1007/s13311-017-0542-y

Jones, K. (2021, September 24). *Psilocybin for Bipolar Depression: A systematic review of risks.* Psychedelic Network. psychedelicnetwork.org.uk/psilocybin-for-bipolar-depression/

Kandola, A. (2017, December 20). What is NLP and what is it used for? *Medical News Today.* medicalnewstoday.com/articles/320368

Kometer, M., Schmidt, A., Bachmann, R., Studerus, E., Seifritz, E., and Vollenweider, F. X. (2012). Psilocybin biases facial recognition, goal-directed behavior, and mood state toward positive relative to negative emotions through different serotonergic subreceptors. *Biological Psychiatry,* 72(11), 898–906. doi.org/10.1016/j.biopsych.2012.04.005

Kraehenmann, R., Preller, K. H., Scheidegger, M., Pokorny, T., Bosch, O. G., Seifritz, E., and Vollenweider, F. X. (2015). Psilocybin-induced decrease in amygdala reactivity correlates with enhanced positive mood in healthy volunteers. *Biological Psychiatry,* 78(8), 572–581. doi.org/10.1016/j.biopsych.2014.04.010

Krause, L. (2020). *What is PTSD?* Very Well Health. verywellhealth.com/what-is-ptsd-5084527

Lea, T., Amada, N., Jungaberle, H., Schecke, H., Scherbaum, N., and Klein, M. (2020). Perceived outcomes of psychedelic microdosing as self-managed therapies for mental and substance use disorders. *Psychopharmacology,* 237(5), 1521–1532. doi.org/10.1007/s00213-020-05477-0

Link, R. (2022, June 20). What is the hippocampus? *Medical News Today.* medicalnewstoday.com/articles/313295#function

Lo, H.-C., and Wasser, S. P. (2011). Medicinal mushrooms for glycemic control in diabetes mellitus: History, current status, future perspectives, and unsolved problems (review). *International Journal of Medicinal Mushrooms*, 13(5), 401–426. doi.org/10.1615/intjmedmushr.v13.i5.10

Ly, C., Greb, A. C., Cameron, L. P., Wong, J. M., Barragan, E. V., Wilson, P. C., Burbach, K. F., Soltanzadeh Zarandi, S., Sood, A., Paddy, M. R., Duim, W. C., Dennis, M. Y., McAllister, A. K., Ori-McKenney, K. M., Gray, J. A., and Olson, D. E. (2018). Psychedelics promote structural and functional neural plasticity. *Cell Reports*, 23(11), 3170–3182.
doi.org/10.1016/j.celrep.2018.05.022

Lyes, M., Yang, K. H., Castellanos, J., and Furnish, T. (2022). *Microdosing psilocybin for chronic pain: a case series.* Pain, Publish Ahead of Print. doi.org/10.1097/j.pain.0000000000002778

Lyons, T., and Carhart-Harris, R. L. (2018). More realistic forecasting of future life events after psilocybin for treatment-resistant depression. *Frontiers in Psychology*, 9. doi.org/10.3389/fpsyg.2018.01721

Matsushima, Y., Shirota, O., Kikura-Hanajiri, R., Goda, Y., and Eguchi, F. (2009). Effects of Psilocybe argentipeson marble-burying behavior in mice. *Bioscience, Biotechnology, and Biochemistry*, 73(8), 1866–1868. doi.org/10.1271/bbb.90095

Merriam-Webster. (n.d.-a). Anecdotal evidence. In *Merriam-Webster Dictionary*. Retrieved December 9, 2022, from merriam-webster.com/dictionary/anecdotal%20evidence

Merriam-Webster. (n.d.-b). Anxiolytic. In *Merriam-Webster Dictionary*. Retrieved December 13, 2022, from merriam-webster.com/dictionary/anxiolytic

Merriam-Webster. (n.d.-c). Neurogenesis. In *Merriam-Webster Dictionary*. Retrieved December 13, 2022, from merriam-webster.com/medical/neurogenesis

Merriam-Webster. (n.d.-d). Nocebo. In *Merriam-Webster Dictionary*. Retrieved December 8, 2022, from merriam-webster.com/dictionary/nocebo

Merriam-Webster. (2022a). Placebo. In *Merriam-Webster Dictionary*. merriam-webster.com/dictionary/placebo

Merriam-Webster. (2022b). Neuroscience. In *Merriam-Webster Dictionary*. merriam-webster.com/dictionary/neuroscience

Microdosing Institute. (2020). Microdosing expert James Fadiman explains the "Fadiman Protocol" [YouTube Video]. In *YouTube*. youtube.com/watch?v=pIisvp3Aihk

*Microdosing Institute|Your microdosing network.* (2020, August 15). Microdosing Institute. microdosinginstitute.com/#

*Microdosing protocols—Fadiman, Stamets, and more.* (2020, November 9). Microdosing Institute. microdosinginstitute.com/how-to/microdosing-protocols/

*Microdosing protocols: The ultimate guide.* (2022). Microdose Pro. microdose-pro.com/microdosing-protocols/

*Microdosing psilocybin and common dosage explained.* (2021, December 16). Reality Sandwich. realitysandwich.com/microdosing-psilocybin/

*Microdosing shrooms to boost productivity and anxiety.* (2021, October 11). Psilocybin World. psilocybinworld.net/microdosing-shrooms-to-boos-productivity-and-anxiety/

Moreno, F. A., Wiegand, C. B., Taitano, E. K., and Delgado, P. L. (2006). Safety, tolerability, and efficacy of psilocybin in 9 patients with obsessive-compulsive disorder. *The Journal of Clinical Psychiatry*, 67(11), 1735–1740. doi.org/10.4088/jcp.v67n1110

Morton, E., Sakai, K., Ashtari, A., Pleet, M., Michalak, E. E., and Woolley, J. (2022). Risks and benefits of psilocybin use in people with bipolar disorder: An international web-based survey on experiences of "magic mushroom" consumption.

*Journal of Psychopharmacology*, 026988112211319. doi.org/10.1177/02698811221131997

Neuro Growth. (2019, August 17). *The dangers of microdosing magic mushrooms every day (you need to know this).* Neuro Growth. neurogrowth.ca/microdosing-magic-mushrooms-daily-dangers/

Nkadimeng, S. M., Nabatanzi, A., Steinmann, C. M. L., and Eloff, J. N. (2020). Phytochemical, cytotoxicity, antioxidant and anti-Inflammatory effects of Psilocybe Natalensis magic mushroom. *Plants*, 9(9), 1127. doi.org/10.3390/plants9091127

Nkadimeng, S. M., Steinmann, C. M. L., and Eloff, J. N. (2020). Effects and safety of Psilocybe cubensis and Panaeolus cyanescens magic mushroom extracts on endothelin-1-induced hypertrophy and cell injury in cardiomyocytes. *Scientific Reports,* 10(1). doi.org/10.1038/s41598-020-79328-5

*Obsessive-compulsive disorder (OCD)—Symptoms and causes.* (2020). Mayo Clinic; mayoclinic.org/diseases-conditions/obsessive-compulsive-disorder/symptoms-causes/syc-20354432

*Paul Stamets "the mushroom man."* (2022, August 16). Mush Love Genetics.

mushlovegenetics.com/paul-stamets-the-mushroom-man/

Petranker, R., Anderson, T., Maier, L., Barratt, M., Ferris, J., and Winstock, A. R. (2020). Microdosing psychedelics: Subjective benefits and challenges, substance testing behavior, and the relevance of intention. *Journal of Psychopharmacology*, 36(1), 026988112095399. doi.org/10.1177/0269881120953994

Pokorny, T., Preller, K. H., Kometer, M., Dziobek, I., and Vollenweider, F. X. (2017). Effect of psilocybin on empathy and moral decision-making. *International Journal of Neuropsychopharmacology*, 20(9), 747–757. doi.org/10.1093/ijnp/pyx047

Pope, B. (2021, January 28). Daniel Carcillo, ex-Blackhawks enforcer-turned-CEO, hopes to heal fellow TBI survivors with psilocybin mushro. *Chicago Sun-Times*. chicago.suntimes.com/blackhawks/2021/1/28/22252803/daniel-carcillo-blackhawks-psilocybin-mushrooms-tbi-concussions-nhl-wesana-health-ceo

*Post-traumatic stress disorder treatment with psychedelic drugs.* (2013). NYU Langone Health. med.nyu.edu/departments-institutes/population-health/divisions-sections-centers/medical-ethics/education/high-school-bioethics-project/learning-scenarios/ptsd-treatment-psychedelics

*Psilocybin health benefits and magic mushrooms microdosing guide.* (2020, June 5). Psilocybin. psilocybin.net/

*Psilocybin is being studied as a potential aid for depression in early Alzheimer's disease.* (2014). Center for Psychedelic and Consciousness Research. hopkinspsychedelic.org/alzheimers

*Psilocybin laws: A country-by-country magic mushrooms legal guide.* (2020). Psilocybin. psilocybin.net/laws/

*Psilocybin therapy: The complete guide (updated 2022).* (2022). Behold Retreats. behold-retreats.com/post/psilocybin-therapy

Raman, R. (2018, June 9). *What does magnesium do for your body?* Healthline; Healthline Media. healthline.com/nutrition/what-does-magnesium-do

Rootman, J. M., Kiraga, M., Kryskow, P., Harvey, K., Stamets, P., Santos-Brault, E., Kuypers, K. P. C., and Walsh, Z. (2022). Psilocybin microdosers demonstrate greater observed improvements in mood and mental health at one month relative to non-microdosing controls. *Scientific Reports*, 12(1), 11091. doi.org/10.1038/s41598-022-14512-3

Ross, D. (2020). Microdosing Psilocybin Mushroom. Independently Published.

Rucker, J. J., Marwood, L., Ajantaival, R.-L. J., Bird, C., Eriksson, H., Harrison, J., Lennard-Jones, M., Mistry, S., Saldarini, F., Stansfield, S., Tai, S. J., Williams, S., Weston, N., Malievskaia, E., and Young, A. H. (2022). The effects of psilocybin on cognitive and emotional functions in healthy participants: Results from a phase 1, randomised, placebo-controlled trial involving simultaneous psilocybin administration and preparation. *Journal of Psychopharmacology*, 36(1), 026988112110647. doi.org/10.1177/02698811211064720

Sandoiu, A. (2019, July 17). Microdosing psychedelics: Does the evidence live up to the hype? *Medical News Today*. medicalnewstoday.com/articles/325773

Schindler, E. A. D., Sewell, R. A., Gottschalk, C. H., Luddy, C., Flynn, L. T., Lindsey, H., Pittman, B. P., Cozzi, N. V., and D'Souza, D. C. (2020). Exploratory controlled study of the migraine-suppressing effects of psilocybin. *Neurotherapeutics*, 18(1), 534–543. doi.org/10.1007/s13311-020-00962-y

Schwartzberg, L., and Monroe, M. (2019). Fantastic Fungi [Video]. In *Netflix*. netflix.com/watch/81183477?trackId=14170045

Sessa, B. (2008). Is it time to revisit the role of psychedelic drugs in enhancing human creativity? *Journal of Psychopharmacology*, 22(8), 821–827. doi.org/10.1177/0269881108091597

Sewell, R. A., Halpern, J. H., and Pope, H. G. (2006). Response of cluster headache to psilocybin and LSD. *Neurology*, 66(12), 1920–1922. doi.org/10.1212/01.wnl.0000219761.05466.43

Siebert, A. (2022, October 12). Microdosing psychedelics is trendy, but does it work? Here's what science says. *Forbes*. forbes.com/sites/amandasiebert/2020/11/13/ microdosing-psychedelics-is-trendy-but-does-it-work-heres-what-science-says/?sh=5005c562cf7c

Sisoian, J. (2020, September 21). *How to keep a journal while microdosing Ayahuasca*. Entheonation. entheonation.com/blog/microdosing-ayahuasca-journal/

Smith, P. (2021, January 31). *Psilocybin and neurogenesis: The long-term effects of magic mushrooms on your brain*. EntheoNation. entheonation.com/blog/psilocybin-neurogenesis-neuroplasticity/

Solis-Moreira, J. (2022, July 22). *Microdosing psilocybin leads to improved mood, less stress in largest longitudinal study yet*. Brain

Tomorrow. braintomorrow.com/microdosing-psilocybin-mood-stress-mental-health/#

*Stacking with truffles, cordyceps, and B12—Microdosing with more energy.* (2021, June 16). Microdosing Institute. microdosinginstitute.com/how-to/stacking-truffles-cordyceps-b12-microdosing/

Stamets, P. (2013). *Paul Stamets quote.* BrainyQuote. brainyquote.com/quotes/paul_stamets_571127

Studerus, E., Kometer, M., Hasler, F., and Vollenweider, F. X. (2010). Acute, subacute and long-term subjective effects of psilocybin in healthy humans: a pooled analysis of experimental studies. *Journal of Psychopharmacology*, 25(11), 1434–1452. doi.org/10.1177/0269881110382466

Sumpter, L. (2022, September 28). *How to dry magic mushrooms.* Zamnesia. zamnesia.com/content/285-how-to-dry-and-store-magic-mushrooms

Swanson, L. R. (2018). Unifying theories of psychedelic drug effects. *Frontiers in Pharmacology,* 9. doi.org/10.3389/fphar.2018.00172

Szigeti, B., Kartner, L., Blemings, A., Rosas, F., Feilding, A., Nutt, D. J., Carhart-Harris, R. L., and Erritzoe, D. (2021). Self-blinding citizen science to explore psychedelic microdosing. *ELife*, 10. doi.org/10.7554/elife.62878

Team Asprey. (2017, February 18). *8 Ways to increase BDNF and keep your brain from aging*. Dave Asprey. daveasprey.com/8-ways-to-increase-bdnf-and-keep-your-brain-from-aging/

Theibert, D. (2021, September 9). *Stability of tryptamines in Psilocybe cubensis mushrooms*. Understanding Entheogens. critical.consulting/post/stability-of-tryptamines-in-psilocybe-cubensis-mushrooms

Thomas, K. (2022, April 13). Safety first: Potential heart health risks of microdosing. *Bill of Health.* blog.petrieflom.law.harvard.edu/2022/04/13/s afety-first-potential-heart-health-risks-of-microdosing/

*Top 10 fascinating facts about psilocybin mushrooms*. (2017, April 11). EntheoNation. entheonation.com/blog/top-facts-psilocybin-mushrooms/

*Top 25 quotes by Albert Hofmann*. (2013). A-Z Quotes. azquotes.com/author/6801-Albert_Hofmann

Totomanova, I. (2020, August 5). *Psychedelics as a potential treatment option in ADHD*. ResearchGate. researchgate.net/publication/348277534_Psyc hedelics_as_a_Potential_Treatment_Option_i n_ADHD

*The ultimate guide to psilocybin mushrooms.* (2020, June 29). Third Wave. thethirdwave.co/psychedelics/shrooms/

Watson, S. (2018, February 22). *Brain atrophy (cerebral atrophy).* Healthline; Healthline Media. healthline.com/health/brain-atrophy

West, M. (2022, April 28). What is treatment-resistant depression? *Medical News Today.* medicalnewstoday.com/articles/treatment-resistant-depression

*What is a strong magic mushroom grow kit?* (2022). Magic Mushroom Growkit. magicmushroomgrowkit.com/what-is.html

*What is psilocybin?* (2014). Psilocybin for Mental Health. psilocybin.health/psilocybin

Wikipedia Contributors. (2022, December 4). *Psilocybin.* Wikipedia; Wikimedia Foundation. en.wikipedia.org/wiki/Psilocybin

Winstock, A., A. (2017). Improved colour blindness symptoms associated with recreational psychedelic use: Results from the Global Drug Survey 2017—JEC Anthony, A Winstock, JA Ferris, DJ Nutt, 2020. *Drug Science, Policy and Law.* journals.sagepub.com/doi/full/10.1177/205032 4520942345

Woon, F. L., Sood, S., and Hedges, D. W. (2010). Hippocampal volume deficits associated with exposure to psychological trauma and posttraumatic stress disorder in adults: A meta-analysis. *Progress in Neuro-Psychopharmacology and Biological Psychiatry*, 34(7), 1181–1188. doi.org/10.1016/j.pnpbp.2010.06.016

World Health Organization. (2016, April 8). *Headache disorders*. WHO. who.int/news-room/fact-sheets/detail/headache-disorders

Zhu, J. (2019, October 23). *Microdosing experience: I microdosed on psilocybin for 30 days, and tracked its lasting effects*. Microdosing Institute. microdosinginstitute.com/microdosing-experiences/i-microdosed-on-psilocybin-for-30-days-and-tracked-its-lasting-effects/

Milton Keynes UK
Ingram Content Group UK Ltd.
UKHW011945170624
444325UK00032B/206